Praise fo

'A complete game plan for grea

'Engaging, inspiring and packed with practical wisdom. It is a flat-out good read.'

—*Outlook India*

'Ageless wisdom, fascinating fables and captivating anecdotes... highly readable, engaging and entertaining.'

—*The New Indian Express*, Chennai

'A stimulating and important book which you should read.'

—*The New Indian Express*, New Delhi

'Golf teaches life's most valuable lessons. Beautifully articulated story and a must read.'

—*Sanjoy Sen*, MD and Group Head of Consumer Bank, DBS

'Finely curated set of life lessons. "Hole in one" *aha* experience for the reader!'

—*Ramky Subramanian*, chairman ICAI Singapore, board member IIFL Finance, banker and advisor

'The distractions of lived experiences overwhelm many, but worry not as Deepak delivers some invaluable lessons to win at the game of life.'

—*Binod Shankar*, executive coach

'This is a terrific story. A must read.'

—*Kulpreet Yadav*, author and actor

THINK
LIKE A GOLFER
WIN
LIKE A GOLFER

Discover **7** Life Lessons From
the Ancient Game of Golf

DEEPAK MEHRA

AMARYLLIS

AMARYLLIS

An imprint of Manjul Publishing House Pvt. Ltd.
• C-16, Sector 3, Noida, Uttar Pradesh 201301, India
Website: www.manjulindia.com
Registered Office:
• 10, Nishat Colony, Bhopal 462 003 – India
Distribution Centres
Ahmedabad, Bengaluru, Bhopal, Chennai, Hyderabad,
Kolkata, Mumbai, Noida, Pune

Think Like A Golfer, Win Like A Golfer by Deepak Mehra

This edition first published in India in 2023
Second impression 2024

ISBN 978-93-5543-808-9

Cover design: Wasim Helal

Printed and bound in India by Nutech Print Services – India

Dedicated to the fond memory of my late father-in-law, Jagmohan Lal Bhasin, a keen golfer and an exceptional leader.

And to my parents, Vijai and Kulyash Rai Mehra, my mother-in-law, Urmil Bhasin, my wife, Ruchi, and my daughters, Shreea and Sstuti, who have always been my support system through thick and thin.

Contents

Hello, Jay

My alarm clock went off at 7 a.m., and like every other day I cursed it before hitting the snooze button. I could feel a throbbing pain in my head as I tried to regain my senses from a tumultuous sleep, something that happened quite often but a couple of aspirin tablets and a strong dose of caffeine always fixed me right up. Last night was a late one, not too uncommon given the nature of my job.

I had hosted the management team of a client company whose order could potentially change the fortunes of my branch, once again place me on top of the league, and set me up for a promotion. But more importantly, at a personal level, this breakthrough would help me realise my ambition of launching my own technology start-up very soon. It was a big win, just in time for the weekend's crucial meeting in Delhi with potential investors for my venture.

Just as I was trying to turn around in bed and force myself to sleep, the alarm went off again. In an instant I sat up with a start, fumbling on the table for the alarm clock. With my eyes barely open, I switched it off, tumbled out of bed and hobbled towards the bathroom. My eyes were burning and the headache was awful. I rushed through my routine in the bathroom, and in less than thirty minutes, I came out fully dressed for my flight to Delhi.

In the kitchen, I saw my sandwich lying inside the microwave, a takeaway coffee cup and coffee powder next to the kettle. Used cereal bowls, crumbs of bread and spilled milk on the table told me my daughters had already left for school. This has been my routine for many years now, ever since I became a vice president. My children are asleep by the time I reach home and would leave for school by the time I wake up. I try to spend some time with them on Sundays, if there are no social engagements and official conference calls.

I knew my wife would have dropped the children at the bus stop at 7 a.m. and then proceeded for her morning walk and yoga in the nearby park with a group of friends. I normally do not see my wife in the mornings.

I heated my sandwich and poured boiling water into the coffee cup. The sugar jar on the table was empty; my children had probably used the last bit for their cereal. As I was looking around in the kitchen cabinets for sugar, my mobile phone alerted me that my car had arrived at the entrance of our apartment block. The flight to Delhi was at 9.30 a.m.—the usual flight I take for the meeting at my company's regional headquarters.

Stuffing the sandwich into my mouth and grabbing my

coffee without sugar, I rushed out with my office bag and the suitcase that was kept ready next to the main door—packed by my wife the previous evening.

The company I work for in India was acquired by a San Francisco-based tech giant, Circo Systems, a few years ago, giving us access to a much larger suite of products that could target many more client industries. To focus on product development and to integrate the Indian business with the rest of the region, the company had moved my boss, the Indian country head, to Circo's Middle East and South Asia headquarters in Gurgaon.

As my car pulled out of my apartment block, I opened my bag, took out aspirin pills and gulped down a couple with coffee. I then pulled out my laptop and started reworking the contract based on the new stipulations agreed upon with the clients last evening. Under an overdose of alcohol and the influence of other distractions, all paid for by my company, the two general managers of the client company had agreed to most of the terms I wanted, and now, before they had a chance to rethink, I wanted to shoot out a revised contract for their approval. Along with this, they had given me a firm assurance that the contract for their entire sales-force automation system would come to my new start-up. I had killed two birds with one stone: business for my employers that would once again make me a star for as long as I decide to stay at Circo, and potential business for my personal venture that was ready for launch any time now.

My college buddy Khosla and I had been working on our start-up idea for a while and had already met a number of investors in Delhi. Our idea was strong and given our industry experience, members of an angel-investor club based in Gurgaon had already committed the start-up capital. After my official meetings on Friday at my company, we were scheduled to meet the angel investors on Sunday and work out the final details of financing. If the meeting went well, we could launch our firm soon with my partner leading the venture full-time while I continued with my job for another year or so. This was crucial because the nature of my job would allow me to feed business to my own venture without the knowledge of Circo Systems.

The Racing Rat

Check-in was surprisingly quick. As I approached my aisle seat, I saw a dignified-looking man in a buttoned-down blue Oxford shirt and khaki chinos handing over his blazer to the stewardess while profusely thanking her and then keeping his bag on the window seat. He must have been in his late fifties but looked fit and athletic.

The seat between us was vacant, giving me some room to spread my papers. As I was taking out my laptop from my office bag, my phone rang. My boss was already in the office and was calling me from his landline in Gurgaon.

'Good morning, Sid,' I shouted, trying to mask the heaviness in my voice and grogginess in my head. I glanced to my left and noticed the man in the blue shirt looking at me with a slight smile.

'Harry, all the area managers except you have already submitted their strategic plan for the launch of our cloud solution. When can I have your plan? San Francisco is waiting for the India plan but your report is delaying the whole process. You know how important this is—this will be our first foray into cloud business in Asia.'

'Sure, Sid. You will have it later in the day. I am working on it now and will complete it by the time I land. In any case, what's the big deal about the strategic plan? Get us the product details from San Francisco and I will start selling it. The only strategy that is important to me is the product, the targets and what it means for our profitability and my bonus.

'And, Sid, good news! I wrapped up the deal with Super Financials last evening and that will, once again, put my revenues ahead of all the others. You know I can't let anyone overtake me.'

'Super Financials? But that belongs to the Bangalore branch. You are again poaching clients from other territories!' Sid snapped back at me.

'Hang on, Sid. You have given me a budget and I have to achieve it no matter what. Correct? That's what you say! And how does it matter to you if it's your left or right pocket? It is all your business! Super Financials has their operations office in Mumbai and the order will be issued from here. It's great I bagged it. The Bangalore guys have been after this account for over a year!'

As I looked sideways, conscious of my raised voice, I noticed the man in the window seat had kept his newspaper down and had turned his head towards me. His bespectacled brown eyes were deep and piercing.

'Harry, I don't like this. We will talk about this when we meet in the afternoon. How about the issue with the new relationship manager? I wonder what's wrong with your office.

This is the second person who has resigned in the last one month complaining about the stressful work environment. Staff turnover in your branch is the highest in the region and a majority of the people in their exit interviews have complained about your aggressive micromanagement. You seem to have ignored most of the complaints so far. You know the head office has no tolerance for such behaviour, right? Please look after your staff and make sure they stay with the company.'

'I will handle it, Sid. You have seen my relationship managers. Most of them are useless. They cannot manage anything. I personally negotiate and close many of the large sales of my branch, and all these guys have to do is to service the relationships given to them on a platter. I wonder what is giving them stress.'

And then, remembering the recent budget discussion, I added forcefully, 'And by the way, Sid, ultimately, what are you looking for? Numbers or happiness of the staff?'

There was silence on the other end of the line. Conscious of the gaze of this enigmatic man beside me, I lowered my voice: 'When we meet today, I want to discuss something that has been bothering me for a while.'

'Go ahead, tell me now,' Sid demanded, sounding irritated.

'You have to take up the matter of my promotion in this quarter's HR Committee. I run your top branch but I am still stuck on grade eighteen while other area heads have crossed grade nineteen a long time ago. What's wrong? Doesn't the company see my worth?'

There was another long silence and then Sid exploded. 'Look, Harry, you have no idea what is required of you. All your actions are placing you on very thin ice, my friend. Let us not even talk about a promotion at this stage.'

I knew Sid well. He frequently lost his cool with me, so I continued: 'I work the hardest, I haven't taken a day off in the last two years, I manage the maximum number of clients, I produce the highest revenue, and I lead the most profitable branch—don't you think this is unfair? When you move to the US next year, don't you want me to run the country business? If I become the country head, you will never have to worry about your India revenues, I assure you.'

A quick glance to the left confirmed my suspicion. The man in the blue shirt was listening intently to my phone call. He looked a little concerned, but he was still smiling. Strange man—why can't he mind his own business?

He was cool and calm in an unusual manner, as if he had no worries in life. He seemed to be just chilling out in his life. Very unfair! Here I am, someone who studied in the best schools, worked hard to get into the top engineering college in India, and then worked even harder to get into the top business school in India, and now slogging my way up the corporate hierarchy with no support or godfather. I am a self-made man and have reached so far through hard work and commitment. At the age of thirty-seven, I am the vice president of a successful software-solutions company in India, and given my performance, I should be soon taking over from my boss.

Anyway, after the rather tense call with my boss ended, I switched on my laptop to start work on the strategic plan for my branch. I had been on it for one week and I knew it would not take more than an hour to finish the document.

As the flight crew made announcements for the take-off, my phone rang again and this time, it was my assistant sales manager, who must have reached our office in Mumbai just then.

'Gupta, I am already in the flight and can't talk now. Just make sure you do not send out any proposals today till I see them. Prepare the proposals and email everything to me. I will review them when I am in Gurgaon and give my approvals. And call the lawyer after some time and check if he has seen my email about the Super Financials contract. He has to finalise it today and it has to be with the client by the end of the day. Actually, leave it. I will call him myself when I reach Gurgaon.'

'But, sir, I wanted to talk to you about Super Financials,' Gupta persisted. 'I have a brilliant idea about how we can position our product to them—it will be a sure-shot sale. Actually, I have done a competitive scan—there is no match for our cloud offering if we add in the CRM and MIS modules and bundle it into an end-to-end solution for them...' Sensing no response from my side, he added, 'How about suggesting our sales-force automation facilities that could help them link up their sales management at a national level without the need for massive capital expenditure—just throw that at a discount...'

'Gupta, you are digressing and totally lost. You don't understand. This is a highly competitive industry. Trying to simply position your own products, bundles or solutions doesn't help. Trying to be principled does not help in real life. That is just for motivational speakers. The game, my friend, is won by beating down competition using any means possible. You have to make the competition look bad. Just making yourself look good will not take you anywhere.

'Moreover, you don't know the latest update, Gupta. I took their GMs of IT and finance to Hard Rock Café last night and then left them in good company. The deal is done. Look, I have a terrible headache and a lot of writing to do on the flight. Please don't call me again during the day. If I need something, I will call you from Gurgaon.' I disconnected the call without waiting for Gupta's response.

And then my phone rang again. It was my wife. I had completely forgotten to call Mira.

'Hi, I am in the flight and ready to take off. Hope everything is fine. On the coming Sunday, keep yourself and the kids free—it has been two weeks since I have seen them.'

'Harish, we are always free. It is you who is either travelling or in office even on the weekends,' was the curt response.

'Come on, you know how important the next promotion is for me. We could be moving to Gurgaon if I take over from Sid next year. Once we are in Gurgaon, I could also actively focus on my start-up and soon I would be free from this drudgery. You know the game plan well... it is just a matter of time, darling! My venture could make us very rich and then I will have all the time for you and the kids.'

'You and your start-up ideas, Harish. Please, I don't want you to waste any more money on these ventures. You have already invested a lot and we have never seen any returns. Do you know that we have such limited savings that I sometimes worry how we will educate our children? All our money has gone chasing your fantastic ideas. The rest goes in paying off loans because you want to live a luxurious lifestyle to impress others while digging a hole for all of us. When will you wake up? We don't want these fake luxuries. We want a peaceful life,' Mira complained in her usual manner.

She was irritating, as always.

'Mira, you will never understand. I am a long-term investor. The funds I have invested in ventures of my friends will one day give us big dividends. Only one of them has to click for us to become millionaires. The start-up I am talking about now is our own. It will belong to us. You don't worry. We still have a lot of time to save up for our children's education... it has a long time to go. And luxuries are important, Mira, if I have to position myself for success. Please do not give me the same crap like always. Now I have to disconnect, the flight is about to take off.'

I should have left it at that but I was too riled up now. 'Hang on, don't disconnect,' I added, just before my wife was about to end the call. Luckily, she heard me.

'Yes, I am here. What is it?'

And then I lowered my voice, conscious of the man next to me, and told Mira, 'By the way, there was no sugar for my coffee this morning. The jar on the table was empty, and I couldn't find sugar in the cabinets. Why do I have to struggle to even get a good cup of coffee in the morning? The bananas in the fridge were all dark and mushy—how many times have I explained that bananas should not be kept in bags? On top of that, the dining table was a complete mess and the kitchen window was again left open—I could see a fly buzzing around. Can't I have some peace in the morning? Why do I have to keep telling you the same things again and again?'

Before I could continue, Mira shot back, 'Harish, you know

what your problem is? Most of the time, you are travelling and staying in hotels, so you expect your home to also be as prim and proper, just like a hotel. You have become a stranger in your own house. You can't even find your own clothes, let alone find sugar in the kitchen. You come home for a few hours, like a guest, and even during that time, you seem to have many problems!'

'Mira, I don't have the time for this discussion.'

'You know what? You are in a rat race. You have no time to rest or relax. You have become so aggressive that even at home we can hardly have a decent conversation with you. You are so possessed by your hunger for power and money that you have forgotten all of us. In fact, you have even forgotten who you are.'

'Come on, don't get started again, Mira. Don't spoil my mood early in the morning,' I said, gritting my teeth.

'And one more thing, Harish. Just remember… even if you win this rat race, you will still be a rat!'

How can you? I was about to shout but decided to keep quiet, given that a few people were already staring at me.

Mira had disconnected before I could say anything further.

As the flight attendant was signalling at me to switch off the phone, my phone rang again. It was Khosla, my partner in our start-up venture in Delhi.

'Good morning, Khosla! I have great news for you… Super Financials will be our first client,' I said in a hushed voice.

I heard Khosla almost squeal in excitement.

'Yes, they have agreed to give us the entire sales-force automation business of their twenty-five offices with over fifteen thousand in-house and external sales agents. Circo will provide the cloud services but the entire sales-force automation will be provided by our start-up. Circo is far too expensive on these services and this business belongs to us, my friend!'

'This order could be over a million dollars for us... but'—he suddenly sounded nervous—'what if your company finds out that you have stolen a part of their business?'

'Don't worry,' I assured him, 'no one will ever find out. I am senior enough to manage it internally. Nothing, not even an email, goes out of our office without my approval. No one in my team is allowed to speak to the senior management without my knowledge. Nothing can leak out. And as far as our venture is concerned, you are the face. No one can ever connect it with me. I look forward to seeing you and the investors on Sunday. With this massive order in our pocket, our first round of funding should be an easy sail. My flight is about to take off... see you on Sunday morning.'

A New Opportunity

The take-off was smooth and I immediately got busy with drafting the strategic document. I hated these documents. What use is an economic update, health of the industry, current practices, gaps in the markets, competitive scan, a SWOT analysis, resource planning, client-service plan and so on, if in the end all that is required from me is to sell and get revenues? Reluctantly, I entered some comments gathered from the meetings and whatever data was available to give it a semblance of a strategic document.

I completed it just as the captain announced the descent to Delhi. The man in the blue shirt was busy with his book during this time. Luckily, he was not one of those social beings who want to strike up a conversation with fellow passengers.

But I was wrong. As soon as the stewardess came to return the man's jacket, our eyes met. He turned and warmly greeted me, 'Good morning, young man. I am Jay.'

'Good morning, Jay. I am Harish Kumar… my friends call me Harry.' I tried to sound friendly even though I was still a bit groggy and in no mood to encourage a casual conversation.

He gave me a broad smile and nodded. I turned my head around and started packing my laptop and papers that were strewn around. I was still wondering how someone could have such a serene smile on his face—was it fake or was this man actually living a blissful life?

As the stewardess returned once again to clear our coffee cups, Jay and I ended up looking at each other again, and this time I thought it would be outright rude if I did not chit-chat a bit. 'What do you do, Jay?' I asked out of courtesy.

'Oh, you know what, I am a full-time player and a part-time worker.' He laughed and then went on, 'Actually, I am a business consultant, and I live in Delhi. And you?'

'I work for Circo Systems in Mumbai. It is a San Francisco-based company, and we are the leaders in software solutions for the financial services industry and soon will be launching our cloud solutions, the first in India. We also have a large software-development centre in India that services the US business.'

I quickly handed over my business card with pride. It read: Harish Kumar, B.Tech (Hons), MBA, Vice President—Mumbai, Circo Systems. 'And what sort of consultancy do you provide?' I asked.

'Harry, I am just a one-man-show. I take up whatever work

Deepak Mehra

comes my way. Here is my business card,' he said, handing over a small, white business card that just read 'JAY' in capital letters followed by his email address.

I looked at the plain card and then turned it around to see if there was more information about him, his phone number or office address. The other side of the card was blank. It was a bit unusual for a person of his stature to not want to share his full name or contact details. Maybe he is one of those people who have a chip on their shoulder or maybe he is just too modest to say much about himself, I thought.

'Jay, you said that you are a part-time worker and a full-time player. Can you explain what you meant?'

'I am happy you caught that. No, I try to work full-time in helping entrepreneurs and businesses but somehow my life and my work have all become play for me. I am not sure where one stops and the other begins.'

'How is that?'

'It is very simple, Harry. Playing teaches me many lessons and introduces me to new ideas that help to make my life and work more rewarding. And then I simply go and share these ideas with others—which is work for me. So, whether I am on the playground or in an office, it does not seem to make any difference now,' Jay replied what seemed to be with his characteristic smile.

'You mean that playing cricket or football gives you new insights into real-life situations? What do you play?' I asked, amused.

'No, Harry, I play golf.'

'Oh, golf—that's a rather slow and relaxed game.'

14

Jay smiled. 'Golf may look slow and relaxed but it is the most exceptional game. The game of golf is the closest to the game of life.'

'But it is a slow and relaxed game, correct?'

'Actually, golf teaches us that there is no fast track to success, only sure and steady steps to victory; hence, it is paced out and looks relaxed. But it is a unique game that carries a hidden message for winning the game of life. Golf is the only ball game where you never tackle, engage, block or confront your opponents. You play with your own ball and try to complete the game in the least number of strokes. You always play your own game. No one can influence your performance. If you do well, it is because of your own ability and attitude, and if you perform worse than others, again, it is due to your ability and attitude. *In the end, it is always you versus you*—whether on the golf course or in life. You know what, I think golf is the perfect metaphor for life. In fact, it is often called the school of life.'

This guy sounded like a mystic! His elegantly aged, clean-shaven face with large, framed glasses and a receding hairline topped with neatly combed, side-parted hair gave him an appearance of a university professor. He had given me a small lecture, which normally I would have brushed aside, but somehow he seemed convincing.

I thought about what he had just said—about the game of golf and what it teaches about life. Clearly, for me, learning about life could wait a bit longer. I still have to achieve something more significant in my career, but the mention of golf did pique my interest.

'I have always wanted to play golf, Jay, but I have never had the time to learn,' I said, trying to sound interested in the subject.

'Are you in Delhi tomorrow, Saturday morning?' he asked.

'Yes, I am. I am busy today and then I have some personal meetings on Sunday. But I'm completely free on Saturday.'

'I play every Saturday morning. Why don't you join me?'

'That is a good idea but I know nothing about golf. I haven't even watched it on television.'

'You will learn. Besides, you will learn a lot more.'

'A lot more... what do you mean?' I asked, laughing.

But Jay responded with a straight face.

'Listen, my boy, I have to make a confession. I overheard all your conversations... with your boss, your junior, your wife, your business partner, and I got to learn a lot about your work, your goals and your life. I have mapped your entire life in the few minutes you were on the phone. And this is what I mean by a lot more—maybe you can learn a trick or two on the golf course that could potentially turn your life and your work into play. You get my point?'

I felt a little annoyed with his confession about eavesdropping on my conversation and then addressing me as 'my boy!' But I let it pass. I was more interested in golf.

'Jay, I don't get your point but I am keen to learn golf and I am free on Saturday morning. Where do we meet?' I asked.

My headache was more bearable and possibly that was the reason I did not react negatively. Maybe because we were a few thousand feet above the ground or maybe it was Jay's cultured mannerisms and suave personality. Under normal circumstances,

I would have blasted him for snooping on my conversations. Somehow it did not bother me when he implied I have to learn a lot more than just golf. Perhaps it was because this man could teach me something that was on my agenda for a while. I knew learning golf would help me in my career and give me an opportunity to expand my business network. Many of my seniors in the regional office play golf. Khosla plays golf and that is how he has networked with all the private equity people and financiers. Learning golf and playing with the who's who would catapult me into the big league. Golf could give me an edge in my job and my new venture.

'Where are you staying in Delhi, Harry?'

'I am staying at the Hyatt in Gurgaon, Sector 68, near our regional office,' I replied proudly.

'Okay, in that case, we should meet at the Damdama Golf Course next to the lake, just a short drive from your hotel.'

'Sounds good. Thank you,' I said, feeling pleased.

'Be there at 7 a.m. sharp. Just remember the dress code on golf courses—collared T-shirt and no denims. When you reach, just ask for Jay.'

'I will be there. And I look forward to playing golf with you,' I added.

'No, you will not play… you will simply learn.'

'Is there a coach who will teach me or will you do that?'

'I will teach you. But for that you will have to become my caddy.'

'Caddy? You mean I will be your helper on the golf course?' I asked, slightly mortified at the thought.

Jay broke into his trademark smile. 'Yes, you will be my

helper and more specifically, you will carry the golf bag around for me as I walk around the golf course!'

I just looked at Jay, not sure what he meant.

'Don't worry, I was just joking!' He laughed, his eyes twinkling with merriment, as the wheels of the plane gently touched down in Delhi.

I had said 'yes' to an invitation without really knowing what lay in store for me. Little did I know that my life was about to change forever.

The Holes in my Goals

I spent Friday at our regional office presenting updates about my branch, discussing new product solutions and negotiating budgets and expenses with the regional guys. I also kept a close control on things in my office back in Mumbai. The discussions with my boss, Sid, about my grade promotion did not go well. For starters, he was upset that we had targeted Super Financials, which was a client of the Bangalore branch. Then, as if he was doing an annual performance review, he brought up the issues of staff turnover, employee-satisfaction survey results, customer complaints and concerns raised by other area heads about the work ethics of my branch, which I believe were all baseless, while completely ignoring the fact that I had delivered top revenues year after year.

Sid said I am too aggressive and did not care about the means when it comes to achieving results. At the same time, I have often heard him chide another vice president accusing him of having a *laissez-faire* approach and pushing him to become more aggressive. It was confusing; if I am aggressive, pushy and deliver results, it goes against me. I could also sense some serious reservations about me taking over the India business. I was very frustrated by the end of my meeting with him. I could see my dreams of making it big within Circo getting completely shattered.

The difficult conversation with Sid kept echoing in my mind and I could not sleep well that night. On Saturday morning, I woke up with a heavy head and did not feel like getting out of bed. But then my eyes fell on Jay's business card which lay on my side table. It reminded me that I was supposed to meet him at 7 a.m. at the golf course. It was 5.30 a.m. already. My first instinct was to cancel the appointment with an apology over a text message.

I picked up his card, took my phone and dragged myself out of bed. As I sat down to send him a message, my mind went back to the brief conversation I had with Jay on the flight. Normally, I would not have let anyone eavesdrop on my conversations, poke their nose in my affairs and get away with that. But there was something magnetic about Jay. He radiated a cool confidence that naturally made me accept his offer to meet at the golf course. I could tell there was something to learn from him apart from golf. Somewhere deep inside I wanted to become like him.

So I changed my mind and decided to head to the golf course. I ordered breakfast in the room, called for a cab and got ready to leave.

With no traffic on the otherwise busy roads, the drive to Damdama was quick. The last ten minutes of the drive was on an undulating landscape along the lake with the backdrop of small hillocks on the far side. Finally, we entered the golf course road, which had beautifully manicured gardens on either side, that ended at the portico of a colonial-style, red-brick building of the club. I was quickly ushered in to an expansive terrace overlooking the golf course. Jay was carefully studying a map that was spread out on the coffee table in front of him.

'Good morning,' I greeted Jay, extending my hand towards him.

'Good morning, Harry. Good to see you. I knew you would come.' Jay stood up and we shook hands. Jay looked fresh and alert. He was wearing a sky-blue polo T-shirt tucked into dark blue chinos, paired with clean white leather shoes.

'Do you start playing so early in the morning, when the sun is barely up?' I asked.

'Oh, yes, the earlier the better... it is nice and quiet in the morning. But today, I will start playing only at eight o'clock. I have kept one hour to explain the game to you, show you the equipment we use, take you around the practising range before we hit the first shot.'

Jay then pulled the tea trolley from the side, gently took the tea cosy off the bone-china kettle and poured some tea for me. The setting was stunning: lush green grass as far as the eye could see with the calm waters of Damdama Lake on the right. The air was fresh, and the golf course had the lingering fragrance of freshly cut grass. I filled my lungs and breathed like I was breathing for the first time.

'Why are you studying this map so intently?' I asked.

'I'll tell you in a minute. But first, take this diary and pen. You may want to take notes about playing the game or anything else you may find interesting,' Jay said, handing over a little red diary with a pen tucked on the side.

'Now, why am I studying this map? See, I normally play at the Gurgaon Golf Club, which is near my house, and I have come to this golf course after a few months. I am trying to understand the layout before we start.

'You see, Harry, unlike any other game, the layout of every golf course is distinct. Even if they are designed by the same golfer, no two golf courses are built alike.'

'That's interesting. But doesn't this complicate the game?' I asked.

'That's the idea, Harry. No two situations in life are ever the same, correct? It is the same on the golf course. You start hitting the tiny golf ball from the tee box or teeing area and then play it over the fairway, which has smooth mown grass, and end up taking it to the putting green area on the opposite end where you have to finally hit it into the putting hole.

'The fairways are not straight patches of grass; they are made in all odd shapes. Some are wide, others are narrow; some are straight while others are dog-leg shaped or bent in the middle. Some can have undulating surfaces while others can have slopes and gradients all along. Moreover, on the way you have to encounter the roughs, or hazards, areas of longer grass, bushes or trees surrounding the fairway. To increase the level of difficulty, there are water bodies, sandpits or traps, sometimes right in the middle of the fairways.

'When you put the ball in the putting hole, you complete one hole on the course. "Hole" here refers to the entire length of the course between the tee area and the actual putting hole in the putting green.

'Championship golf courses, like this one, have 18 holes—18 different tracks from tee area to putting greens. But no two tracks are similar in features.'

'By comparison, all football grounds, tennis courts, billiard boards and even cricket grounds are identical in design and dimensions,' I interjected.

Jay smiled with satisfaction. 'Hence, golf, with its diverse terrain, is called the game of champions. It is not a game of ordinary players who play on known and predictable fields. *The unpredictability of the terrain brings out the champions among the players.*'

'Impressive! But how did golf take on this complicated terrain?' I asked.

'Ah, for that you have to go back in history. It is believed the Romans brought their game of wooden sticks and leather ball to northern Europe. This game gradually became very popular, spread to many countries and was later known as "gowf" in Scotland.'

'Fascinating,' I observed.

'However, the real credit for the development of the modern game of golf goes to a 1457 ruling issued by King James II of Scotland prohibiting the playing of the game of gowf as it was a distraction from archery practice for military training. During that time, Scotland was preparing to defend itself against an English invasion. The ban was finally lifted in 1502 after the signing of the Treaty of Glasgow, which ended over two hundred years of intermittent war between Scotland and England.'

Jay paused to gather his thoughts and then added, 'But something interesting happened during this period of ban on the game. People living in the city of St Andrews, on the eastern coast of Scotland, who wanted to play the game of wooden clubs and ball, had to go outside the city, away from the eyes of the soldiers, to a narrow strip of undulating barren land near the sea. This land was called the "links" because it linked the sea to the land. It was filled with shrubs and high grass, patches of sand dunes and water bodies, fairways or areas that had been cleared by grazing sheep and most important of all, rabbit holes,'—at this point I was beginning to wonder if Jay was some sort of a walking encyclopaedia on the sport—'which probably served as the target goal, or the putting hole, for the ball. And there, at the links, now the Old Course of the Royal and Ancient Golf Club of St Andrews, also referred to as R&A, the game was nurtured for hundreds of years. From there, it has evolved to the great game played and loved by millions throughout the world.'

'Wow, golf carries an amazing legacy,' I exclaimed.

'Harry, it is thanks to the topography of the St Andrews Links that today golf is the only game played on uneven ground.'

Clarity of Purpose

That was a lot of information to take in at seven in the morning, but Jay's enthusiasm was infectious, and I was slowly beginning to get a sense of the game.

'Now I understand why you are studying the layout so carefully,' I observed.

'Yes, so that I have clear objectives for the entire game before I start playing. If you watch a professional golf tournament, you will see top players and their caddies walking the entire course before they play a round. They evaluate the layout of the course, note the hole positions and anticipate potential problems in advance.

'Often, players explore various options to play each hole before they start. They observe the features of the terrain from the tee area to the putting green for each of the holes, calculate the number of shots they will need to hit the ball into each of the holes, the best route to reach the putting hole in the least possible shots, and think of a back-up plan to use if the ball gets stuck in one of the hazards or obstacles and so on.

'The big goal of the game is to complete all the holes in the least possible shots of the ball. The player who completes the course with the least number of strokes is the winner. However, that cannot be achieved unless each of the holes is executed within a limited number of shots. And that requires setting clear objectives for each of the holes on the entire course.'

'Oh, I had never imagined this level of thinking going into a game!' I said, surprised.

'Isn't there learning in this for our life, Harry?'

'Like what?'

'Golf teaches us the importance of clear goal-setting. *A clearly defined goal provides clarity of purpose.*

'And that's not all. Playing 18 holes on a golf course, stroking the ball on an unpredictable and hazardous terrain, can be quite a challenging task and can become drudgery. You cannot see your goal, the putting hole at the far end of the hole, when you start hitting the ball. You cannot see the overall game plan spread over a couple of kilometres of the golf course which you cover over a period of four or five hours hitting a tiny ball,' Jay pointed out.

'But because every player sets their own objective of the number of shots, and then tracks their own progress against their target as they go through the twists and turns of the game, they are driven by a clear sense of purpose, which keeps them motivated and going. Does it make sense?'

I nodded.

'*A big goal or a grand plan keeps us motivated and inspired through the ups and downs of our life.* Let me tell you a little story,' Jay said, rubbing his palms together in excitement.

His eagerness made me chuckle, which I quickly covered up with a cough. Jay seemed like the kind of person who'd have a good story for every scenario.

'One day a traveller came across a large construction site outside a city where a number of stonecutters were working. He was curious and asked the first worker who looked tired and worn out, "What are you doing?"

'"Oh, can't you see? I am cutting stones," snapped the worker and went back to work.

'He came across another worker who seemed to be grumbling, and asked him the same question.

'"Oh hell, I am trying to earn a living!" he shot back angrily.

'Still no wiser, the traveller turned to the next stonecutter, who seemed to be whistling a song and looked cheerful, and asked him what he was doing.'

'"Oh, I have come here to improve my life. This is a huge site. I will have a job for a long time. My children are now going to a better school and soon I will be able to buy a small plot of land in the village," he beamed and then burst into another song.'

With that Jay looked at me and said, 'This is the power of goal setting and working towards a purpose. Everyone lives a life. While most simply drift along, winners are driven and motivated by a clear sense of purpose and direction.

'Harry,' continued Jay, before I could even collect my thoughts on the first story, 'Let me tell you another example of goal setting and clarity of purpose. A friend of mine runs a bakery business with his wife and a small team. At the beginning of each year, they all sit down and list a few holiday destinations— right from the affordable ones to the most luxurious, expensive ones. Then they decide the net profit they must achieve for each holiday destination. They know that if they just about meet their numbers, they will only go to the nearby vacation resort but if they exceed their profit numbers by, let's say, 100 percent, the team could be going to a fancy hill station. Pictures of all the destinations, with the corresponding profit numbers, are stuck on their office walls throughout the year for all of them to visualise where they want to be by the end of the year.'

'Great idea for motivation,' I admitted. Jay sure knew how to make a point.

'And it works—that's the power of a grand plan!' Jay explained. 'Every year they are busting their goals. The business is expanding faster than what my friend had anticipated, and I see them going to the most exotic destinations every year. Isn't it wonderful?'

'Indeed, I get your point very well.'

'So let me ask you, Harry,' said Jay, 'what goals have you set for your life?'

'Goals for my life? I have never thought about that.'

'Think again,' Jay insisted.

I laughed. 'I have been living my life as it comes. I studied well, got a job, got married next and then we had children. Now, I am working on my promotion and planning to start my own venture. At some stage, my children will grow up and later, I will retire. It is the normal flow of everyone's life. It just flows—one event after another. You cannot plan these things in advance!'

'Sorry, you are wrong, Harry', Jay looked at me straight in the eyes. 'If you play ad hoc, your life does not flow. It just passes and soon becomes dull and mechanical. It flows only if you have clear goals to keep your life on track so that you can effectively perform different roles—as a professional, a family member and a community member—and at all times feel propelled and driven.'

I stared blankly at him, not sure where he was going with this.

Clarity of Plan

'Let me make it easy by asking you another question,' said Jay. 'What does success look like to you, Harry?'

If I were true to myself, I had never visualised success. I looked around, thinking hard, and eventually after racking my brain for an answer, I said, 'Lots of money, professional success and fame.'

'Okay, sounds good. So, on a scale of one to ten, how far are you from your vision of success right now?'

'Oh, I may be at three or four. Quite far, I guess.'

'So what is holding you back? Why have you just reached three or four?'

'Well, there are so many things that have to be achieved but the two most urgent ones are getting a promotion at work and starting my own business. I guess these will take me closer to eight or nine straightaway.'

'So what can you do to get a promotion?' Jay asked.

'I think I am working hard to become a top performer in the company so that I can be chosen to take my boss's position when he moves ahead.'

'What else can you do, Harry?'

'Maybe I can impress my boss and do something to get into his good books. Like playing golf with him,' I chuckled.

'Would that help?' Jay asked with a sceptical look. 'What else could you do?'

I thought for a moment. What else can I do? 'Maybe I could network with the people at the regional office. After all they call the shots here.'

Jay did not look impressed. 'Think again, what else? How could you position yourself so that you become the natural choice?'

Seeing that I looked puzzled and a bit edgy, he quickly said, 'We will come back to this later but did you notice what I was trying to do with you just now?'

I was even more clueless. 'No, Jay, I don't know.'

'I was helping you set your goals, assess the current reality and explore options... just like I would do for a game of golf, on a particular course given the conditions on that day and knowing my own skills related to different types of strokes required there. Finally, after exploring all the options, I would have asked you to define your action plan or the way forward. Which options would you pursue and when?'

I was trying to wrap my head around what he had just said.

And then he added, 'This process that I just demonstrated is a powerful framework to set audacious goals and achieve them with ease—just like landing on a massive 18-hole golf course and then putting the tiny ball in each of the 18 tiny holes, one by one, in the least possible shots, while avoiding the hurdles.'

I nodded to signal I was interested in knowing more.

Jay continued, 'This process of planning is called the GROW model. It was developed in the 1980s by Sir John Whitmore, the legendary British sports hero, and has since then become the basis of all performance coaching—whether in sports, in personal life or in business. GROW is an acronym for Goal, Reality, Options and Way Forward.'

Jay then gestured towards the diary, and I handed it over to him. On the first double-spread, he drew this:

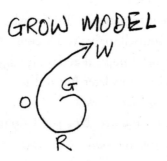

'To set the right goals, you ask yourself questions like: What do I want to achieve in the long term? What will be different when I achieve it? Why is achieving this goal important to me? It is best if you write down your answers on paper,' Jay said while scribbling these questions on the next page.

'You cannot achieve your goal in isolation; you have to take the environment into consideration, and hence the next step is to define the realities. You should ask: Where am I today in relation to the goal? On a scale of one to ten, how far have I progressed? Why haven't I reached the goal yet? What is going on right now? What is holding me back? What are the obstacles? What are my skills and weaknesses in this field?'

I listened carefully and kept nodding.

Jay continued: 'Once you are grounded in reality, you will be able to explore potential routes to reach your goal, their probabilities and pros and cons. *Accepting reality opens up options; fighting reality hooks you to the situation.* You can explore your options by asking yourself: What has worked for me so far? What hasn't? What are my options now? What options do I feel ready to act on? What else can I do?'

'This last one is very important: What else can I do? Keep asking this question till you have explored all possible options— from the obvious to the most fantastic ones. Write down all the answers and their associated pros and cons. And the last step, Harry, is when you really put this planning to work by defining the way forward and asking yourself, "What would be my first step now? When can I start? What will I do on a daily basis? Who can help me on the way?"' Jay continued to speak and scribble in the diary. 'This last step is the operational outcome of the model and establishes the "process goals" for what you have to do every day to achieve those goals. *The path to victory is through small steps.*'

'This is indeed an interesting approach, Jay. I will definitely try it out on myself.'

'Yes, you can do it for any of your goals—big or small. You could use this model for your family goals like spending more time with your children, personal development goals like becoming a better listener or health goals like losing weight. You can start by writing down a measurable goal. Say your goal is losing ten kilograms of weight. The next step in the GROW model is assessing *reality*—defining the current situation. For this you have to honestly answer questions like: What is going on right now? What is holding me back from reducing weight? You may write down answers like: "I eat at irregular times and then end up overeating. I love sweets and desserts. I have to entertain clients often where over-indulgence cannot be avoided. I have no time for exercising," and so on.

'The next step is exploring the *options* you have in order to achieve your goals. You could write down alternatives like physical exercise, fasting once a week, having smaller meals at regular times, cutting down on sugar and alcohol, and so on. Options are not complete till you evaluate their effectiveness and feasibility. For example, you find that a good option would be to add physical exercise to your schedule. So you will need to evaluate whether this is feasible, how you will make time during the week and what you will have to give up to find time for exercising. When you evaluate the next option, like, for example, fasting once a week, you may realise that even though it appears to be effective, it has more disadvantages than advantages. In the end you may come up with more than one workable option. Write down as many details as you can for each of them.

'The final step in the GROW model is the *way forward*. After you have decided on one or two action points, write down an execution plan. For executing the physical exercise option, you may have to specify the type of exercise, how many times a week, what time of the day, how you will find that time, what changes you have to make in your schedule to create time, when you will start and so on.

'Using this framework, you now have a full plan with a timeline laid out in front of you. There is no way you will miss your goal!'

'I think I now understand the model better.' Jay really brought home the fact that clear goal-setting can open up limitless possibilities in my life.

Then after a pause, he continued, 'You could also use this model to help others achieve their goals, your colleagues or your family members, including your children. You can coach anyone with this model.'

Seeing me nod, he said, 'Try it; it really helps. And do you know why it is effective?'

I looked at him expectantly.

'Because, Harry, all the answers belong to the person being coached. The role of the coach is limited to asking the right questions. The options or action plans that come out of the probing process belong to the person being coached; they have arisen from within that person. These solutions are not a set of advices from the coach. You see the difference—realisation versus advice? With realisation, the person being coached is likely to take full ownership of the plan and be more committed to implementing those action plans.'

It was indeed an excellent lesson in goal-setting. I thanked Jay. 'Brilliant. I like this model.'

'However, your journey towards success is still not complete. There is another hurdle to cross,' Jay said, looking towards the green fields.

'And what is that?' I asked.

Clarity of Priorities

Jay paused to have another sip of tea when someone from the golf club walked in with some papers. Jay immediately stood up and shook hands while the other person bowed out of respect. The person was carrying some forms, which Jay signed, and then handed over a card, which looked like a scoring card, and left.

Jay sat down again and continued explaining.

'So, there is one more hurdle. This model of goal planning proves that your mind is the beacon for all the information you need for achieving your goals. Think about it for a moment—your mind naturally follows the GROW model when it is working on achievements: what is my goal, what is my current situation, what options do I have and how do I proceed from here. It flows well. All the answers are already within you. Despite this, you cannot hear yourself clearly. Why?'

I thought for a moment to come up with something clever to say but all I managed was a 'Because...'

'Harry,'—thankfully, Jay quickly took over—'at any point in time we have a cluster bomb of goals that we are trying to achieve. The brain is trying to do a lot of thinking at the same time and hence the busy mind loses focus.

'Look, the game of golf teaches us that we have to go through one hole at a time, with all our ability, and move to the next hole only when the existing hole has been successfully completed and the ball has been putted in the hole. There is no moving on unless we have completed the first one. You cannot leave a hole incomplete or midway and move to the next one. You see the difference between golf and other games. In cricket you can get out at any time or you may have to stop batting once the innings is over. In football you may never hit a ball into the opponent's net because your job may be to simply defend if you are playing backfield or just pass the ball on to your colleagues if you are playing midfield. But in golf every player has to traverse the same path—from tee to putt, and finish each and every hole.'

'So what you're saying is,' I hurriedly interjected, in an attempt to make up for floundering like an idiot a minute ago, 'just like how in golf one can win only by focusing on one hole at a time and not worrying about the forthcoming holes, similarly in life, one must work on one goal at a time?'

'Well, no, Harry, that would be impractical,' said Jay genially.

Darn it! I probably jumped the gun here. I decided it's best I let Jay do the talking.

'You see, my boy, every goal we set for ourselves creates a little bit of stress, and having too many big goals means carrying a small slice of fear from each of the goals at all times. That can easily cripple the mind. The objective should be to focus on a few goals at a time and do a good job of them before moving to the next.' Jay smiled at me with satisfaction, probably because I looked like an eager student desperately trying to grasp every word that his favourite teacher was uttering.

'To learn about focus,' he went on, 'we have to turn to Warren Buffett, one of the richest and the most successful stock market investors in the world. He uses a three-step process to help his employees focus on their goals. In fact, there is an interesting story that has made his process famous. One day Buffett was talking to Smith, one of his senior executives, about his life goals. As step one, Buffett asked him to write down the top ten things he wanted to achieve in his life. So Smith took some time and jotted them down,' Jay said as he handed over the diary back to me.

'In fact, why don't you write down your top ten life goals here, on this page? I will show you Buffett's process firsthand!'

'Okay, you want me to write them down now? It will take some time,' I replied.

'No problem, take your time. Just write anything important that comes to your mind—stuff that you want to have but do not possess now.'

Thinking hard about my life goals, I wrote down the following:

LIFE GOALS

1. 5 million dollars
2. Holiday home in the hills
3. A BMW Car
4. Tech start-up
5. Country Head of Circo
6. Author a best seller
7. Send children to US Univs
8. Fame and respect
9. Physical fitness
10. Good family relationships

Jay looked at the list and signalled his approval.

'Buffett then moved to step two. He asked Smith to review each item and circle the top three goals that were the most important to him at that time. Why don't you do the same, Harry?'

'But all of them are important to me. How can I select only three?' I complained.

Jay laughed. 'This was exactly how Smith had responded too. After all, that is why he had written them down after a lot of thought. But Buffett insisted he could pick only three, not even four. Why don't you do the same, Harry? Go ahead!'

I started scratching my head.

Deciding the top three was not as easy as I had thought, and at one stage I was stuck. 'I am pretty sure about a couple of goals but I am confused between some. For example, working towards having five million dollars in my bank account or physical fitness. Can you help me with this?'

Jay thought for a moment and then clarified: 'So the secret of Buffett's planning process is selecting those top three that are the most important in the present moment, not some time in the future. Moreover, select those that will facilitate your progress to the other seven. Tonight, this week and this month what is the most important—five million dollars or a good night's sleep? What is more important? Working for the next ten years to accumulate five million and then try to improve your health when it may actually be too late? Or focus on physical fitness now, become more energetic and more productive during the days that can in turn make the journey to five million dollars much easier?'

This was an 'aha' moment for me. Was I chasing the wrong goals all this while? I erased the circles around '5 million dollars' and instead circled 'physical fitness'. I used the same logic and erased the circle around 'holiday home in the hills' and circled 'good family relationships'. I followed the logic of 'What will lead me to the other?' Would a holiday home help us improve our relationship or having good relations at home help me reduce my stress levels, make me more relaxed at my workplace and probably help me achieve more in the professional sphere? The choice between 'Country head of Circo' and 'Fame and respect' was easy. Given a choice I would like to position myself as a respectable professional at a much bigger platform than Circo. However, considering my rat race, I could not think beyond my little world. With my new-found clarity, I knew that there were things bigger than Circo—professional excellence, industry leadership, respectability—things that will provide fulfilment and contentment in the long run.

This is how my list looked now:

LIFE GOALS

1 5 million dollars
2. Holiday home in the hills
3 A BMW Car
4. Tech start-up
5. Country Head of Circo
6. Author, a best seller
7. Send children to US Univs
8. Fame and respect
9. Physical fitness
10. Good family relationships

Jay took another look and asked, 'Are you sure these are the most important goals in your life today?'

I nodded in affirmation.

'Congratulations, Harry. You have just defined a vision for your life. You now have clear goals for your personal and professional life.

'Smith did the same for Buffett. Warren Buffett then asked how he would achieve these goals and what the implementation plan was. I am not sure what Smith said but if I were in his place, I would have made a plan based on the GROW model. What do you think?' Jay asked.

'Yes, I think the GROW process would be very helpful in planning each of my top three goals,' I agreed.

Jay then resumed his narration: 'Once the top three planning sessions were over, Buffett asked Smith, "But what about the other seven items that you didn't circle? What is your plan for them?" Smith immediately replied, "Well, the top three are my main focus but the other seven come just after that. They are still important so I will dedicate lesser time to them. They are not urgent but I still plan to put some effort behind them."

'To Smith's surprise, Buffett jumped in his chair and responded in a firm voice, "No, you have got it all wrong, Smith. Everything you did not circle just became your not-to-do list. No matter what, you will not pay any attention to these goals until you have succeeded with your top three."'

Jay stopped, allowed this to sink in and then asked me, 'Surprised with Buffett's response?'

'Yes, very interesting,' was all I could say. I was still trying to process what he'd just said.

'Harry, this is the power of elimination. Step three of the Buffett Process is elimination. *To focus on a few goals, you have to eliminate the rest.*'

'The other seven items on your list are important to you but till you achieve your top three goals, these are mere distractions. Spending time on achieving them is the reason you can have ten half-finished projects instead of three completed ones. So eliminate ruthlessly and focus on your *core* goals.'

'It is no surprise that Warren Buffett has done so well. He has just focused on a few goals. While investing in businesses, he has stuck to industries he understands and has totally avoided industries that were the flavour of the season or in fashion. For example, till very recently, he stuck to food, financial services and manufacturing while totally avoiding technology. The world has been going crazy investing in technology stocks since 1990 but Buffett refused. He simply considered them a distraction from his bread-and-butter businesses like Coca-Cola; Kraft-Heinz, which makes cheese and ketchup; and Gillette, which was later bought by Procter and Gamble; and continued to make billions every year without any roller-coaster rides.

'Over the years, people have implored him to run for the US presidency, become a board member of companies, write books, give interviews or speak to students. He has stayed clear of these distractions and only focused on his core goals.'

This point about focus struck a chord with me.

The Way to GROW

Jay shifted in his chair as he said, 'You see the reason why I was so engrossed studying the layout of the golf course? It gives me great clarity about what I am going to achieve and how.

'From defining my goals, using the GROW model and

41

following the Buffett Process, I have learnt that the difference between struggling and winning, both on the golf course and in life, is driven by the three Ps of clarity:

'Clarity of Purpose. What I am going to do and why.

'Clarity of Plan. How I am going to do that.

'Clarity of Priorities. Which of my goals I am going to work on first.

'And, you know what, clarity provides motivation and reduces ambiguity, which reduces stress and in turn improves my performance—whether I am hitting the ball on the golf course or living my day-to-day life. *Clarity of purpose, plan and priorities keeps the spirits high even when the going sometimes gets tough.*'

'In golf, as in life, every game is won before it is played. *Winners win first and then go to play while losers go to play and then try to win.* You see the difference, Harry? This difference between winners and losers is clarity.

'Think about it carefully, what are you working for? What is your grand plan? Are you crystal clear about your purpose, plan and priorities?'

Jay had made many valuable points so I opened the diary to quickly scribble them down lest I forgot them.

'But clarity is just the beginning, Harry. You have won the game but the game is still waiting for you,' Jay said, rather cryptically.

Mindset 1: Clarity
Win Before You Play

Winners win first and then go to play while losers go to play and then try to win.

Take a shot:
What is your Grand Plan for life? Think through and define the key objectives in different spheres of your life—work, home, family, relationships, health, and society.

Use the GROW model to focus on your goals.
Then use the Buffett Process to eliminate your goals.
You are all set for success.

Playing that Dog-leg Bend

J ay poured some more steaming hot tea into our cups. The person from the golf club came back, this time carrying a large and tall beige-coloured leather bag slung over his shoulder and gently kept it against one of the chairs. It looked very heavy. Jay turned around and thanked him. The bag had JAY embossed on it in black.

'Ah, we should start playing soon,' Jay exclaimed. 'But I have something to show you first.'

And then taking the diary from me, Jay turned a page and started sketching something.

'Harry, I want you to look at the layout of the first hole on this golf course.'

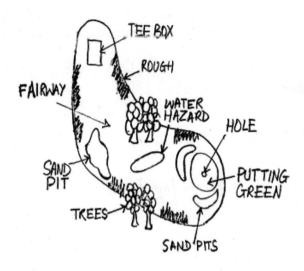

Jay kept the diary on the table in front of us and started explaining his sketch. 'The aim of golf is to start hitting the ball, or tee off as it is called, from the tee box, and then carry the ball with a number of shots over the smooth fairway, while making sure the ball does not get stuck in one of the hazards or obstacles such as bushes or tall grass, sandpits, water hazards or trees. In the end, the objective is to putt the ball in the hole, or cup, at the putting green. Every time a player accomplishes this task, he completes one hole. The player who completes it in fewer number of shots gets a lower score, and at the end of all the holes, the player who has the lowest score wins.

'Let me make it a bit more interesting,' Jay said, getting up and pulling the tall leather bag towards himself. He unzipped one of the side pockets of the bag and took out a small white ball.

'Look at this,' he said handing over the ball to me. 'The golf ball is about four centimetres in diameter—merely the size of a large lemon—whereas the length of the entire track between the tee area and putting hole can range from two hundred to four hundred metres.'

'What if a player hits the ball and it lands in one of the hazards?'

'The player has to concede one shot, basically count it as an extra shot, and start the game by placing the ball on the fairway closest to the hazard. So it is like a penalty. However, if it goes into the sandpit, you are allowed to enter the pit and hit the ball out and continue.'

'A bad move can set you back?' I asked.

Jay pulled over the map of the golf course. 'Yes, and to make it more complicated, the golf tracks are often made in odd shapes. Some are narrow with water bodies running on both sides, leaving no room for risk-taking. Others have large sand tracks and bushes completely blocking the track, leaving no option but to take big risks with the shots.

'And then you have some holes like this first one,' Jay pointed towards his sketch again, 'which are sharply bent in the middle in an L-shape. We call it a "dog-leg" shape in golf.'

I smiled at the creative way of naming the shape.

'Look at this. The fairway turns sharply to the left and therefore your target, that is the hole in the green, is towards your left. But to ensure that you reach the green in the least number of shots, you have to tee off and drive the ball to the right rather than driving straight towards the green on the left.'

'So you play blind, without any sight of the target?'

Jay smiled. 'Not only that. Look carefully at the design of the fairway. On my first shot, if the trajectory is not perfectly straight, the ball could land in the large sandpit which covers the entire side, waiting like a magnet for a slightly errant shot.

'If you land the first shot well, you will get a clear view of the target, the green with the flag in the centre.'

'So the second shot should take you to the green?'

'Not yet,' Jay said pointing to the map again. 'On the next shot, your ball has to fly over this massive water body and then land near the green while avoiding the sandpits that flank the green. Any miscalculation can be costly.'

'But, Jay, rather than taking these long and sometimes blind and risky shots, why can't we just hit a number of shorter shots which would take the ball to the target without the risk of getting stuck in any of these hazards?' I suggested.

'Aha! Then you don't stand a chance to win. Remember what I just said? The player who completes all the holes in the fewest number of shots wins.'

'Oh, of course. That was silly of me,' I realised. 'So there is no way out. Risks cannot be avoided!'

Step Into Your Fear Zone

'Harry, risks cannot be avoided. And you know what, you progress only when you step out of your *comfort zone* and into your *fear zone*.'

The mention of 'comfort zone' triggered something in my mind. My boss would keep telling me to get out of my comfort zone—not realising how hard I worked and how much I sacrificed for the company. I always failed to understand what this term actually meant.

'Jay, I get your point about taking risks – I have taken many risks in my life. But what do you mean by comfort zone? The fact that I take risks means I am outside my comfort zone, doesn't it?' I asked.

'Not necessarily, Harry. Your comfort zone is your pattern of thinking. Taking risks may not take you out of the zone, and you may just do more of what you are doing, using the same thought processes and acting in your usual style. *Real risk-taking is breaking your pattern of thinking.*'

Jay could sense that I was at sea here, so he came up with a few anecdotes for me.

'Charles Dickens, the famous British writer, wrote a story of a man who was sent to prison for some petty offence but languished there for many years. He used to always dream of being a free man, to walk out of the prison, meet people and enjoy the sunshine. Then one day his wish came true. He was released and escorted out of his cell, past the narrow and dark corridors, and outside the main prison gate into the hustle and bustle of the town centre. But within a few minutes of freedom, the man turned around and started pleading with the prison guards to take him back to his prison cell.

'The fast-moving horse carriages, hawkers shouting at the top of their voices, busy people rushing around the streets and the general pace of city life scared him. He wanted to go back to the familiar confines he had got accustomed to.

'His physical confinement had grown to become his mental confinement. The thought of being a free man was too overwhelming. The very thing he wished for now scared him. He was scared of change. He wanted to go back to his comfort zone, even if it had some drawbacks.

'Many of us have big dreams of doing great things. But these things will never happen if we keep turning away from the sunshine of freedom and going back to the darkness of our prison cells.

'What are your prison cells, your comfort zones and your thinking patterns that you do not want to give up? Think about it, Harry. You have to identify your comfort zones and work on them, for these are holding you back from achieving your true potential.'

Picking up the diary and turning a page, Jay illustrated his point:

'We remain stuck in our little circle, totally oblivious of what magic exists outside. Magic happens when you step out of your comfort zone and cross the wall of fear. *Magic happens in your fear zone.*'

I tried to wrap my head around this concept and think about my comfort zones.

But as if reading my mind, Jay said, 'One's comfort zone is very comforting, and change is always difficult and scary.

'Your comfort zone could be your view about your success. You may have a firm view that your peers are competing with you and hence you always deal with them with a sense of apprehension and fear. That may not allow you to really position yourself as a senior and mature professional within the organisation. Your fear zone lies in acting in a more mature manner, patiently holding back when the urge is to respond to provocations with full force.

'You may have a comfort zone of close friends with whom you can let your hair down, chat nonsense for hours and spend your evenings in different pubs trying out new spirits. Breaking away from them and this sort of pointless socializing to create time for personally uplifting pursuits can be uncomfortable. Your fear zone lies in getting left out of their social circle.

'Your comfort zone may be staying late in bed on the weekends rather than breaking away and creating time for family, physical fitness, reading, learning a new skill or developing a hobby.

'Your comfort zone may be your idea of relaxation; slumping in front of the television and binge-watching the latest smash hit drama while munching on loads of comfort food. If you are on a mission to improving physical fitness, you have to become conscious of your calorie intake and get out for some tough physical workouts regularly. However, to adopt this new lifestyle, you have to endure some pain and depravation. Your fear zone lies in the pain and depravation of missing out on television time and the delicious but unhealthy fast food and desserts.

'Very often limiting beliefs or religious superstitions create comfort zones. You mould your entire life around these irrational beliefs. Your fear zones lie in breaking those superstitions and facing the dreaded consequences that you assume may befall you.'

I found myself leaning forward in my chair because many of the points he highlighted applied to my life.

'Think about yourself, Harry. Where are you and where do you want to be? Are you ready for the future? What do you need to change in yourself? What are the walls of fear holding you back?' Jay asked, pointing towards the wall he had drawn on the sketch.

I could see various aspects of my life playing out in my mind. Jay had earlier talked about clarity of purpose, planning and priorities—I had to work on changing the way I approached my goals and plans; I had to pull myself away from my little world where I blindly chase worthless goals and instead, expand my horizons to bigger and more meaningful achievements.

To step out of my comfort zones, I would have to let go of my habits, behaviour and attitudes—in my career, health, family life and social life. I had to revamp my entire life, which would require a great deal of effort. Where do I start?

'Jay, what you are saying makes a lot of sense, but I am not very sure how to break the walls of fear that hold me from breaking out of my comfort zones.'

Jay was quick to answer. 'Harry, these walls are made of bricks that represent your habits. Every time you repeat, you add another brick to the wall. *The walls of habit are generally too weak to be felt, but over time they become too strong to be broken.*

'So the answer to your question lies in gradually chipping off your habits. Look for all the habits and beliefs that you hold very dear to you. These are the bricks that make up your wall of fear.

'You cannot break the wall in one go but to begin with you can stop adding more bricks to the wall. After that, start removing one brick at a time. Attack the smallest habits or beliefs first and gradually move further. *Do one thing every day that scares you.* Try breaking one of your long-held superstitions and see what happens. Say hello to everyone you pass by in your residential complex or office, even if you don't know them. Strike a conversation with a complete stranger. Go a day without social media or a week without television. Leave your mobile phone at home when you go to the grocery next door. Try to stay silent and listen more to others during a heated debate in the office. Take a new route to your office—never mind that extra few minutes on the road. Walk up the stairs instead of taking the elevator. Take a cold shower in winter, even if it is extremely uncomfortable. Listen to a new genre of music that you have never heard before and try to appreciate it. Read a book or go out for a jog instead of watching television...'

As I pictured each of his suggestions in my mind, I was convinced I could try them all.

'None of these things will kill you,' Jay declared, 'but they will slowly help you explore your fear zone. With time, increase the stakes and try to shed bigger habits, thoughts and ideas. With time you will be able to remove many bricks, and then one day the wall will suddenly crumble and disappear. And then watch the magic unfold in your life. You will become fearless. You will become free. The world will be your oyster.'

Jay's exposition on breaking free from one's comfort zone was like a shot in the arm. I felt super-motivated to break my old habits and explore new things in my fear zone. I took the diary from Jay and quickly jotted down some notes.

Jay picked up his tea cup and leaned back in his chair. He had a little smile on his face.

Let Go of the Cows

'Let me tell you a Zen story,' Jay said with a smile. 'While travelling through the country, a wise man and his disciple came across a hut in a remote desolate area and were surprised to find a very poor couple, their three children and a bony cow living there. They were curious to know how these people survived in that inhospitable place. The head of the family said, "Look at this cow. It gives us milk. We drink a little and make cheese with the rest. Then I go to the market in the nearby town and exchange it for food and other essentials. That is how we survive." The wise man wished him well and moved on. After crossing into the forest, he said to his disciple, "Go back and take the cow to somewhere in the jungle where they cannot find it again." The disciple was confused and said, "Master, they will die if we do this." The wise man was outraged at the disciple's impudence and repeated his orders. The disciple did as he was ordered to do but was ridden with guilt after that. He kept thinking about the family. He wanted to go back and find out what had happened to the family, apologise to them and help them.

'A few years later, when he got some time off from the wise man, he immediately rushed to the desolate area where the hut was. But he could not find the hut or the poor family. In its place stood a big house with a garden where he could see three smart-looking teenagers and their parents celebrating with many guests. Hesitantly, he approached the man in the garden and asked him if he knew what happened to the poor family that once lived in the same place. The man said, "We are that family." The disciple was dumbfounded. "A few years ago there was nothing here. You were very poor. What did you do to improve your life in such a short time?" The man smiled and said, "We had a cow that kept us alive. She was all we had. But one day she disappeared. To survive, we had to start doing other things and develop new skills. One idea led to another and today I have a flourishing business.""

'So you see, Harry, we have to look for these cows in our lives that are keeping us miserable. We may think these are essential for our happiness but in reality they may be binding us in shackles, holding us back from progress.

'I started my career in a large multinational company. It was my dream job. I worked very hard. I was rapidly promoted to bigger roles managing larger regions. With that came more work and more travelling. I was spending lesser and lesser time at home. Bigger roles also meant spending more time dealing with the bureaucracy and politics of a large multinational, and lesser time with the people who worked with me. I felt I was becoming less creative and more machine-like. I knew my situation was taking a toll on my mental and physical health but I had never imagined the world outside my company. Like a frog in a well, my life was limited to my company, its people and its business. If my work was unfulfilling then all work in the world was unfulfilling—that was my limited view of life. Leaving my job to escape the misery was unimaginable.

'Then one day I bumped into a classmate who was working at a senior position in a small local company. Chatting up with him I realised that he was leading a very different life, both professionally and personally. He probably earned a little less than me and did not carry a fancy title on his business card and did not travel internationally on business trips and seminars, but he was far happier than I was. He spoke about the books he was reading, his hobby of teaching at orphanages, the weekend activities with his children and the latest movies that they had watched. I was completely stunned. I had never imagined that a person could lead a normal, balanced life if he was working in a responsible position in his career.

'I realised that my job, with a monthly cash flow, was like a cow that gave me a false sense of achievement and happiness. In reality it was holding me back from achieving the full potential of my life. When I shared my realisation with my family, they jumped with excitement and that set me on the journey of self-employment. I resigned from my job and in due course became a successful consultant. It was not easy in the beginning, but letting go of my cow opened up a whole new world of abundance for me. We have to identify such cows in our lives and let them go. *What you hold on to holds you back.*'

The idea that we all hold on to such cows immediately resonated with me.

'Jay,' I said, thinking back to the time I had held on to my 'cows', 'when the stock market collapsed, I was so shocked and taken aback that I decided I would never invest in stocks again. Since then, I just kept my money in bank deposits, feeling very comfortable with the stability of value. These bank deposits became my cow that held me back from my financial freedom. In this period, the stock market index more than doubled and my portfolio, had I not sold it at a loss, would have grown six-fold!

'And the worst part... now I am taking risky bets on start-up ventures to make a quick buck and make up for the lost time in the stock market.'

'That's one cow that you have identified,' Jay smiled. 'Look for more. You are probably holding on to bigger ones! These could be ideas, beliefs, mindsets, relationships, social or professional arrangements or anything else. Think hard, find them and let go of them. *Winners do not fear change—they go looking for it.*'

Upgrade, Upgrade, Upgrade!

'Harry, let me show you something else now,' Jay said, as he unzipped the leather bag from the top. He pulled out about ten or twelve golf clubs and laid them on the table between us.

It was quite a range of equipment. All the clubs had a long, thin metallic stick with a grip on one end and a small head, about four- or five-inches wide, on the other. Some were longer than the others; some had large, rounded, bulb-shaped heads, some had leaner and rectangular heads, while one of the shortest ones had just a straight bar-shaped head at the end.

'Wow, why do you have so many types of clubs?' I asked.

'The reason is simple: the golf course has a diverse landscape and one type of club cannot function optimally across the entire area. The ones with these big rounded heads are called woods, and these ones with lean, rectangular heads are called irons. These irons with slanting faces are wedges, and this one here, the shortest club with a bar-shaped head, is a putter,' he said, pointing towards the different clubs.

'And how do you decide which one to use?'

Jay picked up a few of them as he spoke. 'The woods and irons help you in long and lofty shots: woods to tee off and irons on the fairway. The wedges help you in short and lofty shots when you are playing near the putting green or to stroke the ball out of a hazard. And the putter helps you in short and rolling shots on the putting green.'

'What a wide range!'

'A golfer needs to learn and master a range of skills. They have to be equally proficient in using woods as irons or putters. You cannot play the entire hole using just one club. If I just give you a putter to play the entire course, you will not be able to hit long and lofty shots. If I just give you a wood to play, you will not be able to play the short and calibrated shots. Without a range of tools and the ability to play with each one of them, you will get stuck.

'Just like a golf bag full of clubs, each one of us carries a bag full of skills—hard skills, soft skills, relationship skills and life skills. These skills allow us to navigate through life—which is constantly changing whether we realise it or not. If you ever feel you are stuck and not progressing—either in your personal or professional life—then know for sure that you are missing some skills. *Feeling stuck is a signal to upgrade your skills,*' Jay advised.

Then as an afterthought, he added: 'My boy, don't you upgrade your smart phone regularly—but when was the last time you upgraded your personal operating system?'

I chuckled. But I wondered what Jay meant by upgrading

our skills. I knew everything that I had to know for doing my job; after all I had a top-notch educational degree and held a senior position in a multinational tech company.

'Harry, as we grow up in life, we keep acquiring new skills for evolving phases of our lives. You are now a vice president of your company and are responsible for a large business. How have you evolved over the last few years?'

'Well, it has been a huge change. I now handle a large team, and my revenue achievements have gone through the roof. I am responsible for the profitability of my business and for hiring and firing people. I am now competing head on with much more competition than before. It is a massive change,' I explained.

'No, Harry,' Jay said while shaking his head. 'What has changed in your day-to-day work and responsibilities?'

'It has stayed the same, Jay. I was doing sales, and I am still doing sales. Even though I have a large team, the team members are all useless. I still have to meet all the clients and close large transactions myself. The only thing that has changed is the workload and pressure,' I said, almost complaining.

'Is your boss appreciating your efforts?'

'Unfortunately, Jay,'— I sighed deeply—'he seems to be biased against me. He is refusing to give me a promotion.'

'Do you feel stuck, Harry?'

'Absolutely.'

'What did we just say, my boy? Feeling stuck is a signal to upgrade your skills!'

'Hmm...?'

'Harry, it's simple. When you were a junior, your boss wanted you to be a good salesperson. When you were promoted to heading your branch, the boss wanted you to manage the branch, not be the best salesperson. Your job now is to develop other sales people so that you can do bigger things like analyse the markets, look for gaps and opportunities for new products, plan resources and focus on market leadership and positioning of your brand.

'You have to change your tools and style with changing circumstances. If we resist change, we will be stuck where we are!'

This was a revelation for me. Why did I never think of this before? Was this the reason the other branch managers in my company were all senior to me even when I delivered the highest numbers? It suddenly made sense. Was my boss really biased or was he just unhappy with my style of management—doing everything on my own, no delegation and no development of staff?

I think the answer was painfully clear. I had to upgrade my professional skills.

Jay knew what was happening in my mind. Maybe he was bringing up this issue because he had overheard my conversation with my boss.

He was not done yet. He asked another probing question. 'You are married and have kids, right? Sorry,' he said with a sheepish grin, 'I overheard your phone conversation in the plane.'

'Yes, you are right. I have two children,' I said with some degree of scepticism, trying to figure out where he was going with this.

'So how has your personal life—your life at home—changed at a day-to-day level from the time you were a bachelor?'

I could get his drift but I decided to be frank with him. 'Look, Jay, I work very hard in the office and I have to travel a lot. I am not in town very often but when I am back in town, I have to catch up with my friends and social circle.'

As I said this, I immediately understood what Jay was coming to. But as usual, I rambled on, digging myself a deeper grave. 'It is only fair that I spend time with my friends who I have grown up with, and what is wrong with hitting the pub just after office? This is what all successful professionals do all over the world!'

Alright, so Jay had baited me, and I fell hook, line and sinker. I had not changed my style at all since my bachelor days which explained why I felt stuck in my family life. Jay's words rang in my head: Feeling stuck is a signal to upgrade your skills. So, I must upgrade my life skills to align it with my current stage.

Jay looked at me with amusement. He laughed and said, 'You spoke about successful professionals? Keep in mind, professionals may be spending their evenings and nights in pubs but *successful* professionals do not!'

I could only give him a quizzical look in response.

'Some of the greatest, smartest and richest professionals who are also successful human beings are teetotallers. They may all have had a different lifestyle when they were younger but as they progressed, they also changed their style to suit the demands of their higher levels of responsibility. Did you know that billionaires like Warren Buffett, the most successful investor in the world, Bill Gates, the founder of Microsoft, Mark Zuckerberg, the founder of Facebook, Steve Jobs, the founder of Apple, and Sundar Pichai, the CEO of Google, do not drink alcohol? They want their mental faculties to be in top form, and they want their days to be positive and productive, not numbed and impaired by hangovers and headaches.

'Harry, *pleasure may be available in pubs but greatness is not served there,*' Jay stated.

Wow! That was the first time someone's words had hit me so hard. I was silent for a while. I had nothing to say. I had to upgrade my personal attitudes and habits—Jay had made a very strong pitch.

As I was reflecting on his words, Jay started packing up his things. The map was folded and put in the side pocket of the bag. The golf ball and the scoring card also went in along with that. Next he picked up the golf clubs, one by one, and started placing them back very carefully in the bag—with their heads on the top. He zipped up the bag and rested it against the chair. I think he was getting ready to start the game.

Jay probably sensed from my prolonged silence that his message had hit a nerve, so he quickly changed the subject.

'Okay, tell me, Harry, which is your favourite food joint in Mumbai?'

'Why?' I asked with amusement.

'You will soon know, but tell me, please.'

'Hands down, it will be Masala at the Taj Palace Hotel.'

'And which dish do you like the most at Masala?'

'Oh, nothing in particular but the chef always surprises us with his creations.'

'Is there any other food joint that you frequent?'

'Yes, that is Tehrani, a tiny restaurant in the narrow lanes behind the Taj Palace Hotel.'

'Aha, and what do you like there?' Jay continued to probe.

'Oh, I always go there for their kebabs and Persian bread. It is the most satisfying food on the planet.' I said, salivating at the thought of the kebabs. 'And, Jay, I have been going there since I was a kid. Their kebabs have a distinct taste and flavour that have not changed since then.'

'And how do you think they maintain the consistency of their taste?'

'Well, they say they have a secret recipe which has been passed down the generations... probably a couple of hundred years now.'

'Wow! Can you guess who earns more—the chef at the Taj or the cook at Tehrani?'

I just laughed. 'There is no comparison between the two. The chef at the Taj probably earns a hundred times more!'

Jay looked satisfied. 'That's the point, Harry. The chef at the Taj is flexible. He can whip up any recipe based on a customer's whim or on the availability of ingredients. He can come up with a new menu almost every month of the year—correct? And he can do it with ease because he has developed his versatility by going through formal culinary education and practice.

'On the other hand, the cook in Tehrani follows a recipe. He does not innovate or experiment. Even if he wants to be innovative, he will at best come up with a variant of his kebab.

'Now, don't get me wrong. We cannot overlook the question of opportunity here. The cook in Tehrani and the chef in the Taj probably did not receive the same exposure and opportunities. But, I would like you to just focus on the concept of cook versus chef.'

Jay then took the diary and drew this illustration:

'The words chef and cook seem like synonyms and are used interchangeably. But in reality there is a world of difference between the two,' Jay explained.

'I learnt this lesson from the writings of Tim Urban, where he tries to find the secret sauce behind Elon Musk's trailblazing success. Elon Musk, the founder of Tesla, is like a chef. He reasons from the first principles—the very foundation of a problem—and then comes up with ground-breaking and out-of-the-box business ideas. No wonder he is such a prodigious entrepreneur solving big ticket problems from environment preservation and road safety with autonomous electric vehicles, making space more accessible with SpaceX, global internet availability with Starlink, connecting human brains with computers with Nuralink and so on. By comparison, normal entrepreneurs are like cooks—their work is a version of what is already out there. Some try to improve upon it and hence are more successful, but they still remain cooks, maybe innovative cooks. A chef is a leader while the best of cooks are merely followers.'

'Wow, I had never thought about this,' I said while thinking about the cook versus chef analogy.

'Isn't is fascinating, Harry,' Jay continued, 'there are cooks all around—in every field... be it business, politics, entertainment or even in our social circles. But only a few chefs—and these people are 100 percent creators, and leaders—are disproportionately rewarded for their approach.'

'You are right, Jay. I never thought in these terms.'

'So whatever you do, Harry, think whether you are playing a cook or proceeding like a chef.

'Golf carries the same message about leadership—play like a chef rather than a cook. You have to be flexible to play in different terrains of the golf course, which are as diverse as our life—some flat while others uneven, some straight while others bent in different shapes, some smooth while others full of hazards and obstacles. Golf does not have standard, copy-book style shots or manoeuvres that players can implement in given situations. Every golf course in the world is unique and throws up twists and turns in the game that require out-of-the-box thinking. There is no precedence to refer to or copy from.

'Makes a lot of sense, Jay!'

'Golf also carries a clear message about facing challenges with courage, Harry. Let me explain this with a story from American author Ryan Holiday's book *The Obstacle Is The Way*. Sounds like a paradox?'

'Yes, it does. How can the obstacle become the way?' I responded.

Jay chuckled. 'Listen to the story and you will get it!'

'A benevolent king felt his people had become too soft and entitled. They were losing their ability to face challenges or strive harder for progress. He wanted to teach them a lesson and came up with a simple plan: Early in the morning he would block the main entrance to the city with a large boulder and then hide nearby to observe their reactions.

'What would the people do? Would they try to remove the boulder or would they get discouraged and turn around?

'At the crack of dawn, villagers started coming on the main road carrying their produce to sell in the city. One by one they reached the massive rock, looked at it, complained loudly and turned around to take the longer route into the city. None of them tried to do anything about it. The king was disappointed.

'Finally a frail-looking peasant reached the impediment. He thought for some time, parked his vegetable cart on the side and went to the forest nearby to look for something to use as a lever. He came back with a long branch which he cleverly leveraged to dislodge the heavy boulder and clear the path.

'And to his surprise the poor farmer found a purse of gold coins under the rock with a note from the king, which said: *The obstacle in the path becomes the path. The obstacle is the path.*'

'Nice, isn't it?' Jay smiled as he completed the story. 'Whenever we face hurdles we have a choice to make: we can either be blocked by them or we can choose to advance through them, above them and beyond them. "The obstacle is the way" is not a paradox. In fact, it is the ancient art of turning adversity into advantage.'

Wow! I loved the story and the deep meaning hidden in it.

'So now you know why the golf course is dotted with hazards, roughs, sandpits, water bodies and other impediments. It is trying to teach an important lesson for life. Every obstacle can throw you out of the game. And there is no way to avoid obstacles. You have to play through them. You have to overcome them with courage. Playing it safe does not work. It will just slow your progress. Every time you overcome a hazard on the golf course, you feel more confident and become stronger, which is exactly what is required to win the game! Faced with courage, every adversity turns into an advantage.

'Harry, if you face challenges with courage and without fear, every impediment to action offers an opportunity to advance and progress. You cannot give up and you cannot look for an easy way out. You have to get out of your comfort zone and into the fear zone. After that, every impediment you overcome rewards you with more strength and more courage. *What stands in your way becomes the way.*'

Jay's words were impressive.

I opened my diary once again and scribbled some more. Even as I was writing, Jay stood up, picked up the bag and slung it over his shoulder. 'Ready to start?' I asked.

'Yes, soon. But are you ready to explore another paradox, Harry?'

Another paradox? I gave him a puzzled look.

Mindset 2: Courage
Let There Be Change

Winners do not fear change; they go looking for it.

Take a shot:
Think hard and look for your comfort zones. Look for what you think gives you happiness but in reality is holding you back. Think about the 'cows' that you can let go.

Have you upgraded any of your skills lately—hard, soft, relationship and life skills? Upgrade your personal operating system and upgrade your trajectory of growth.

Think about how you handle obstacles to your goals. Do you get discouraged or do you face them with courage and advance upwards and onwards? Remember, the obstacle is the way!

Could I Swing It?

'Yes, the paradox of passion,' Jay declared grandly as he started walking. I quickly gulped down the last sip of tea, picked up my diary and followed him.

The word 'passion' resonated with me. I lived passionately and worked passionately. It was with passion that I became what I was. I had the passion to be number one in whatever I did; no one could ever challenge me because I was driven by passion.

But paradox in passion? What did that mean? From the terrace we walked back into the building and then down a flight of large stairs that took us to the ground level. We walked out where a number of buggies were parked, and along with them were a few three-wheeled trollies to hold the golf bags. Jay pulled out a trolley and mounted his bag on it.

'Here you go. This is now your responsibility, caddy!' he said jovially.

I pulled the trolley along as we walked onto the narrow brick-laid path towards the golf course and kept wondering about what this paradox of passion meant.

Rather than going towards the course, we headed to a location with a number of small tee-off areas in a row. It was like a practice area for golfers. Except for a couple of golfers at the far end, most of the practising stations were empty. Golfers were striking their ball into the large grassy area in the front.

Jay reached the first station and announced, 'We are now on the driving range. Every golf course has a driving range for players to practise and perfect their swing, the process of executing a perfect shot. After all, *following the process is the ultimate goal of a winner*. If they get their swing right, the game is in the bag!'

'And what are those numbers written on the grassy area in the front?'

'Those are distance markers indicating the distance you have to hit the ball, in yards, and here we have a bucket of balls to practise with.' He picked up a few small wooden pegs lying on the side. He pinned one of the pegs on the ground and mounted a golf ball on it.

'This peg is called a tee. It raises the golf ball above the ground to make it easier to hit. This is allowed only for the first stroke from the tee area.'

Jay was getting ready for a shot. 'Now that the ball is mounted and ready to be hit, we must learn how to hit it.'

'Let me take out the wood for you,' I offered, opening the bag.

'That will be the biggest wood, 1-wood, which is the longest among all the clubs and is also called the driver.'

With the driver in his hands, Jay moved towards the centre of the tee area. 'Harry, now watch carefully how I hold the club.'

I saw Jay holding the grip of the club in his left hand, with his palm open, while gently resting the clubhead on the grass in front. He then folded his left fingers over the shaft. Next, he brought his right hand just below his left hand and deftly interlocked the two together.

'This sure looks like a very carefully formed grip, Jay.'

'It is all in the grip. Let me show you,' he said while handing the driver to me. 'Let the clubhead rest on the ground with the grip in your left hand. Fold the fingers over it in such a way that the thumb is on the shaft, facing down. Now bring your right hand just under the left on the grip. Make sure the small finger of the right hand is curled over the index finger of the left hand.'

I did as I was told and Jay was happy.

'Now come, stand here and hit the ball.'

'Why don't you do it first? I would like to see,' I said, not sure about hitting the ball.

'Okay, here you go.'

Jay gripped the club, stood at some distance from the ball and positioned the club behind the ball that was resting on the tee. He was quite a distance away from the ball since the driver was a really long club. He then bent forward a little, straightened his back, bent his legs a bit, practised a few swings in the air and shook his legs a bit.

Following this, he swung the club all the way towards the right till the clubhead was behind his back and then smoothly swung the club back down hitting the ball with a very pleasant and crisp 'zing' sound. The ball flew away straight above the grassy area and landed somewhere just after the 200-yard mark. The tee was uprooted and landed a couple of feet in front of us.

The entire process of swinging the ball and then launching it in the air looked easy and effortless.

Jay looked pleased. He then replaced the tee and placed another ball on it. 'Now you try, Harry.'

I gripped the club as he had shown earlier, and took my position where he was standing before. I placed the clubhead just before the ball, straightened my back and bent my knees a bit to loosen them. I then swung the club all the way back and brought it down with all my strength to whack the ball. There was a swoosh of the shaft moving in the air as I swung the club down, but I did not hear the expected 'zing'. The golf club completely missed the ball and twisted all the way to the other side.

'Try again.'

I tried again. This time I practised a few swings in the air and repeated the entire motion. Swoosh and nothing. Missed again.

'Try again.'

I repeated the set of motions very consciously and came down hard on the ball. This time I was lucky. After the swoosh, I heard a 'thwack'. The ball was knocked off the tee but rather than flying up, it hit hard into the ground. It just bounced and rolled a few metres ahead. What a pity.

'Where am I going wrong?'

'Show me your palms.'

I opened my palms for him.

'See, they are blood red.'

'What does that mean?' I asked, surprised at my own hands.

'I will explain, but first let us look at the swing. Do you know why you missed the strokes and finally when you hit, you hit it to the ground?'

'I guess the driver's long shaft makes it difficult to strike a small ball,' I said, trying to analyse my folly.

'Yes, but the driver is the longest among the clubs so that it can impart the maximum amount of energy to the ball and carry it far onto the fairway. So that is by design. The reason you missed the stroke is that you did not execute the swing correctly.'

'And what is so special about the golf swing?'

'Oh, the entire game of golf depends upon the swing. It is very special. A golf swing is a circle with three parts. The first part is the backswing. If you remember my swing, I took the golf club all the way back, behind my head till the left shoulder was under my chin. Then I rapidly, but smoothly, brought down the club in a downswing, which is the second part, till the clubhead hit the ball. The swing was still not over yet. The swing continued on its third leg called the "follow-through", which took the club all the way around to the other end. A good follow-through ensures accuracy of the direction and avoids deviation from the flight path. Think about it... even a one-degree deviation in the angle of the launch can land the ball many metres away from the target spot.'

Be a Smooth Operator

'After missing the ball the first time, you became too focused on hitting the ball and that led to tension in your shoulders and arms. Your shoulders became stiff and rather than hanging loose, they straightened. That pulled your arms back, towards your body, and your clubhead missed the ball again, this time by a bigger distance. A smooth swing is possible with loose, flexible shoulders and freely swinging arms like a flywheel on its axle.'

'If your shoulders and arms are loose, how do you generate the power in the stroke?' I enquired.

'Power in the swing comes from the movement of your shoulders and torso on the pivot of your hips. It is like your whole upper body adding its weight and imparting momentum on the small clubhead through your arms and the club shaft. This entire momentum will then be smoothly transferred to the tiny ball that takes off like a rocket. Power does not come just from hitting the ball hard. You don't have to be all buff to send the ball two hundred yards away. Anyone can do it if they just follow the process. In fact, the golf swing has a profound lesson hidden in it. An easy and well-executed swing teaches us that *the smooth and fluid wins where brute power fails.*'

I was now beginning to understand where I went wrong.

'Now let us come to the second part of the problem: your grip. After swinging just three times, your palms became blood red—correct?'

'Yes, but what does that mean?'

'Harry, the reason is the same. You were focusing on hitting the ball hard rather than focusing on the mechanics of the swing. After missing the first stroke, your tension rose and with that your grip on the golf club became even tighter, in anticipation of a more powerful swing. But a tight grip restricts the movement of the wrist. If the wrist does not move smoothly, it cannot transmit the momentum from the body to the club.'

Jay walked to a sandy patch near the path and beckoned me to follow.

'Come here and show me your palm. I want to pour some sand over it.'

'Okay, Jay. Here you go,' I said sportingly, getting up and walking towards him. I knew Jay had some trick up his sleeve.

I opened my hand wide and held it out. Jay picked up a handful of sand from the course and dropped it on my open palm. 'Keep your palm wide open; don't try to hold the sand,' he said.

The sand quickly spilled out and only a little bit was left in the centre of my palm.

'Let's do it again,' he said, picking up another fistful of sand. 'This time, close your hand as tightly as possible to prevent the sand from spilling out.'

I did as I was told. As he poured sand on my palm, I closed my fist tightly.

'Tighter,' he said.

The dry sand again slipped out of my closed fist leaving just a few specks in my hand.

Jay looked happy at his experiment and its expected results. 'You see, whether you have no grip or if you have a very tight grip, all the sand slips out. To retain the maximum amount of sand in your hand, you require a grip that is just enough— neither too tight nor too loose. You have to make a little cup between your fingers and the palm to gently carry the maximum amount of sand with you,' he said, picking up some sand again and holding it in his palm.

'The tasks and situations you manage, your relationships and even your family are like sand. If you try to control too hard or micromanage, people slip out. And if you do not engage with them at all, they spill out. Think about it,' Jay said, a trifle smugly.

'Harry, the best example of how micromanagement can destroy value is of Steve Jobs before he was sacked from the same company that he had founded. Due to his passion for product design and performance and his great attention to detail, Steve Jobs came up with a highly differentiated product, the Macintosh, which revolutionised the personal computers market. But his micromanagement of the company and meddling in every little function led to multiple issues—the chief being his inability to retain talented managers—and eventually the board had to ask him to leave Apple Computers in 1985.

'Once when Steve Jobs was walking into his office building with board members and senior delegates, he saw water sprinklers getting installed in the lawns. He made all of them wait for twenty minutes on the sidewalk while he stepped off and gave detailed instructions to the landscaping team on the exact placement of the sprinkler heads.

'In fact, the term micromanager was an understatement for him. He used to be called a nano-manager!'

The mention of micromanager immediately reminded me of my boss Sid's comments about my style of management. I could now relate to that. I still review every client proposal issued by our branch. That was fine when we were a two-person office but now the team has grown and I have managers who should take full responsibility of their business. But since I insist on micromanaging, we often have delays in sending out proposals. In a few instances we have lost business. The same is the case with approval of leave for the staff. Every leave approval comes to me just because it was the process when we had a handful of staff. Very often we have resource planning issues because too many people from the same team are on leave at the same time. However, their managers can do nothing because the approvals are always given by me. Micromanaging has become counterproductive in our office. And I never realised that. Till now.

I was also reminded of my many pet peeves with my wife about how things should be kept in the kitchen or in the refrigerator. Micromanaging every aspect of the home even when I hardly spent any time there!

Gentle Persuasion

While Jay was talking to me, he was also hitting the balls from the bucket. One after the other, he was connecting the club with the balls and lifting them high into the air and so far that I could only see them after they landed on the far side of the driving range. It was a pleasure to see how effortlessly he played. I guess that is why they say those who make it look easy have relentlessly worked hard to reach this point.

'I am sure you have heard the classic Aesop fable about the Sun and the Wind,' Jay said.

'Yes, I think so but why don't you refresh my memory?'

Jay was happy to narrate the story. 'One day there was an argument between the Sun and the Wind about who was stronger. They argued for a long time, giving reasons and counter-reasons but could not decide the winner. Before long they saw a traveller walking down the road. That's when they had an idea. They challenged each other: the one who succeeded in removing the man's coat will be the winner.

'The Wind volunteered to try first. It began to blow hard, raising gusts of air, making it harder for the man to take a step forward. The Wind continued blowing harder and harder but the man held on to his coat tighter and tighter. After some time, the Wind was exhausted and gave up.

'It was now the Sun's turn. The Sun looked at the man and started shining gently on the road. The man looked up and was surprised by the sudden change in weather. The Sun did not spend much energy nor did it apply any effort. It just continued to shine gently on the man's head. Soon the man started feeling warm and beads of sweat started dripping from his forehead and covering his face. Unable to bear the heat, the man finally took off his coat and headed to the nearest tree to sit down and rest.

'Moral of the story?' Jay asked. '*Gentle persuasion is a powerful force*. Winners succeed by gentle persuasion rather than by using coercion or fear.'

In my mind I could picture myself being more of the Wind rather than the Sun—whether at home or at work.

Jay carried on. 'We often come across situations where we try to drive change among others. This could be persuading our colleagues to change their product focus, or convincing our business partners to reduce their prices, or compelling our children to reduce their time spent on social media, or other similar positions. Our default mode of management is the age-old "carrot and stick" principle—either show them a reward for their actions or scare them with punishment or dire consequences. Unfortunately, both the approaches do not lead to any lasting change.

'Harry, among my own clients, I often see professionals who are committed to getting results. They attempt to push through hastily, forcing things in a particular direction and working hard, but they end up getting only mediocre results. They believe if they have a strong business case, if they can work hard, assert enough power, build enough support, they will be successful in driving their agenda forward.'

This approach appeared familiar to me too, so I nodded vigorously.

'Unfortunately, while many of those elements are important for success, that approach rarely works. It may deliver fantastic results in the short term, making them a darling of their bosses or their shareholders, but over the medium term, these executives end up tired and frustrated, thinking that everyone else is dragging their heels. They burn bridges, break working relations, demoralise their teams and eventually become a burden on the system. The same bosses who earlier loved them for their drive and aggression now dump them for causing too much of collateral damage. Does this make sense, Harry?'

'I can identify with what you are saying. I have experienced it as well,' I said, thinking more about my own struggles. I was mostly pushing my agendas, demanding things from others, pushing them, following up with them, hounding them and even shouting at them with either a 'carrot' or a 'stick' in my hand. And interestingly, despite all the effort and energy I wasted on them, I did not see any improvement. I think what I lacked was impact and influence, which comes from a deeper level of engagement with others, as Jay mentioned, and was totally missing in my case.

The Paradox of Passion

By now a few more people had come to the driving range close to where we were standing. Jay knew a few of them and quickly waved at them. He then turned around and looked at me. 'Let me demonstrate what I just said.'

'I know these two gentlemen there,' he said pointing towards the end of the driving range. 'Let's go sit on the bench and watch them strike the balls.'

'The one on the left is Satya, a very successful entrepreneur in Delhi and a client of mine. Look at how effortless and easy his shots look. He takes his time to prepare for every stroke; he loosens his body and executes the stroke taking care of every little detail of the swing. Notice how consistent and accurate his shots are. He works smart—in his work and on the golf course.'

Then pointing to a well-built and muscular young man, he said, 'The one on the right is Ash. He currently works for a multinational and has changed three jobs in the last five years. Now, watch him. He's been coming here for years, working really hard but not changing his techniques. He rushes through his preparation, grips the club like he is trying to strangle it and then tries to muscle the ball down the range by hitting it as hard as he can. His follow-through is just a process of him trying to stop his club. On the course, you can often see him frustrated, looking fatigued and worked up. His shots go all over the place. He works very hard—on the golf course and in his profession as well.'

Jay hadn't finished yet. 'Satya always follows the process without worrying about the outcome. He leaves the outcome to the process. He trusts the process.

'Ash follows the process sometimes, but he is usually in a hurry to achieve the outcome. He has more faith in his muscular strength than in the process. The outcome is in front of you.'

The difference between Satya and Ash was very evident from the quality and consistency of their shots. Even though we were sitting at a distance from them, I could sense that while Satya was very comfortable and composed, evidently enjoying his time, Ash was jumpy and agitated and was obviously not having a good time.

'There you go, Harry, another lesson that a golf swing teaches us about winning in life. *Winners worry about the process, not the outcome.*

'Rather than focusing on the result, a good golfer focuses on the mechanics of his swing. That's it.

'If you focus on the little parts of the process, the outcome will take care of itself. However, if you start worrying about the result, you are likely to make a mistake in one little component of the process, which will then end up ruining the shot.

'Passionate attachment to the outcome of your efforts can reduce the chances of success. Winners always remain *detached*.'

What Jay said about detachment did not go down very well with me. 'Look, Jay,' I blurted out, 'I have read about this concept of detachment, and now you are saying the same thing. I cannot get my head around this. It sounds like a paradox.

How can I be detached and still achieve my results? How can I not be passionate about my work? How can I be detached from what I am doing? If I do not put my heart and soul in the job at hand, there is no way I can achieve anything. Passion and drive give me the power to get ahead in life.'

Jay nodded as I spoke. 'My boy, passion is important to provide motivation but it has to be handled with care. When passion turns into an obsession, it can lead you down a path of struggle rather than victory. The word "passion" is derived from the Latin word for "suffering" – unbridled passion only leads to suffering, not achievement. We may be motivated by stories of great achievers who blindly followed their passion but may be unaware of their failures in the other aspects of their lives.

'Blind passion can shrink your life – you may totally focus on work while ignoring your real life. An obsession may force you into taking shortcuts that may later backfire. Obsessive passion can make you a slave of external goals and external validation. And a blindly driven person can be devastated even by a minor setback, steering him out of the game completely.'

As we sat on the bench and talked, Jay was exercising his feet and legs. Then he stood up and did a series of bending and stretching exercises.

'We should get going but before that let me tell you one of my favourite childhood stories, Harry.'

'This is a story of a king and his loyal bodyguard. The big, muscular bodyguard protected the king and followed him like a shadow. In the court he would not allow people to come very close to the king and on the streets he ensured that the king was kept safe from his enthusiastic fans. One day the king was having a nap when a house fly entered the chamber and sat on the king's face. The king was disturbed and waved it away and went back to sleep. But the fly would not go; it would fly away for some time and return to the king's face. The passionate bodyguard was watching this for a while and became very angry. He took out his sword and started chasing the fly around the chamber. As the fly sat on the king's face again, the loyal bodyguard hit the fly with all his might. The fly flew away unharmed, but the king was dead.'

Jay burst into laughter as he ended the story.

'Very often we carry the sword of blind passion and goal obsession with us and strike at the wrong places—quite literally in the case of the king's bodyguard—burning bridges with people, pushing us back in our mission and jeopardising our own interest in the long run.

'Blind, passionate obsession is the hallmark of a struggler. Winners are driven by self-awareness and detachment. Detachment from the outcome, not the efforts. Do you see the difference?' Jay asked.

'Jay, I must confess that I often behave like the king's bodyguard. If there is a crisis in office, I cannot control myself from hurling expletives at people or throwing papers on their faces or just stomping around shouting at the top of my voice. I am so obsessed at achieving results or resolving issues that I lose control over myself.'

'Your self-awareness is the first step towards detachment. I am happy that you are able to observe yourself dispassionately,' Jay said in an encouraging tone.

'*Winners are closely attached to their efforts but detached from the results – they live with an attached detachment.* Attachment to the effort means that you should execute your tasks in the best possible manner. Be mindful of what you are doing at that very moment and do it well. If you are on the golf course trying to swing your club, stay detached from the result. In any case, the golf course is so spread out that you cannot clearly see your goal, the little putting hole. However, you know that the only way to reach that goal is by perfectly executing the shot that you are playing, which will take you closer to your goal. There is no point worrying about whether the ball is going to land on the fairway or in a sandpit or the rough.

'The more you worry about the end result, the worse your performance is going to be—just like a while ago when you were trying to hit the ball.

'Shall I regale you with yet another Zen fable?' Jay asked with a hint of a smile.

'Of course,' I replied immediately.

'A man was eager to receive the kind of adulation he had seen people lavish on a Zen master. He came to the master and enquired about the length of the course to become a spiritual teacher.

'"Ten years," replied the master.

'"What if I studied twice as hard?" asked the man.

'"Twenty years," said the master.

'"What if I studied three times as hard?"'

'"Thirty years," came the reply.

'"How can that be?" enquired the confused aspirant.

'"When one eye is fixed on the fame and glory of achieving

your goal," said the master, "only one eye is left to find your way."

'We often get so anxious about the end result that the anxiety itself becomes a roadblock, hindering our progress. On the other hand, if we are passionate about putting in our best efforts, the likelihood of success increases on its own. So where should we direct our passions—towards efforts or towards outcome?' Jay asked.

'Efforts,' I accepted immediately.

'*You should have passion for efforts, not outcome,*' Jay said in a definitive tone.

I think for the first time I figured out what this 'attached detachment' concept really meant.

Be Not a Worrywart

Everything Jay was saying was very logical. However, I still had some doubts.

'Jay, I get your idea of detachment and the concept of following the process but how do I practise that in my day-to-day life?'

'As concepts, these may sound simple but they are difficult to implement,' Jay replied. 'Fear and anxiety hold you back from getting detached from outcomes. Worrying about the future is one of the major activities of the brain—that is how human beings have survived so many dangers since prehistoric times. So there is no point fighting your basic instinct. However, you can train yourself to look at things differently.'

'But even that is easier said than done,' I remarked.

'You know what, I use a simple technique to train my mind to significantly reduce the overhang of worries that we tend to carry with us.'

Jay took my diary again and opened a new page. He drew a table with three columns and named them 'Can Control', 'Can Influence' and 'Cannot Control': 'Harry, every time you are worried about too many things that are not going as per plan, draw up this table and start noting down your worries under these three columns. For example, meeting the deadline to submit a report to the head office is in your control and will, therefore, go under the first column. Saving money and investing it wisely for the future or maintaining good relationships in the family or at the workplace are common worries for all of us. The solutions to resolving these issues cannot be found by anyone other than us. These are entirely in our control and will go under the first column. We cannot wish these worries away, we cannot forget them, we have to personally work on these worries and find sustainable solutions.

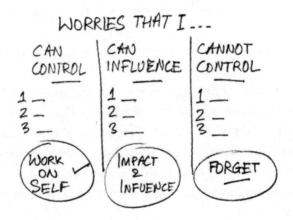

'However, achieving revenue budgets for the quarter is not directly under your control. You can only influence the actions of clients or others in your team to achieve your revenue target; therefore, you put that under the second column. Similarly, ensuring your children study well is something that worries you but you do not have direct control over it. You can only influence that by providing good opportunities and helping them with their studies. So that goes under the second column as well.

'But your health and fitness, quality of your sleep, mental attitudes, emotional wellbeing, which are the foundations on which you build your personal and professional life, are entirely in your hands; you have to put in conscious efforts in these spheres of your life. Hence, these would go under the first column.'

I nodded in agreement.

'Then there are other things you cannot do anything to change. For example, what you have said or done in the past, the mistakes you have made, the conflicts you have experienced, what your competitors are doing or what is happening in the overall market. These worries should be written under the "Cannot Control" column.'

'Or where the ball lands after you have hit a well-crafted shot from the tee area.'

Jay grinned broadly. 'Absolutely!'

'If you start making a list of all your major worries right now, I can already tell you there is very little that will go into the third column. I can assure you most of your current worries or challenges will fall under the first or second column.'

'What about the perception people carry about me? I have no control over that,' I stated, sounding resigned.

'Do you really think so? I think it goes under the first column. You are delivering top-notch revenues, but that has not helped. Now, if you consistently display true leadership skills, integrity, team spirit and cooperation with your colleagues, I am sure you can change people's opinion about you. It may take time, but it is within your control. It should be jotted down in the first column.

'However, the behaviour of your peers, subordinates and business partners or even your family members cannot be fully under your control. Here, you have to use gentle persuasion. After all, they will react to what they experience. You change their experiences and they change their behaviours—simple. So how people behave with you is something that goes under the second column.

'After you have put down your worries or challenges in these three columns, jot down a couple of action points for each one of them. The actions under the first column relate to "Work on Self", while those under the second deal with "Create Impact and Influence". What actions would you take for the third column, Harry?'

'Nothing, I guess,' I responded.

'Correct, so stop worrying about them. They are not in your control. You cannot change them. Accept them as they are and move ahead or move around them.

'If you have no control, what is the use of worrying? If you have control, what is the use of worrying?' Jay asked with a chuckle.

Mindset 3: Detachment
Trust the Process

Winners are attached to their efforts but detached from the results.

Take a shot:
Do you often find yourself pushing hard to get your way in day-to-day life? Practise gentle persuasion and see the magic unfold.

Do you often worry about the future? Can you try to focus on the right efforts, in the present, so that the future is automatically secured?

A Face-off with Myself

Jay had started walking towards the golf course. I grabbed the trolley and followed him.

'It is almost eight o'clock. Let's proceed to the first hole.'

We walked back on the narrow cobblestone pathway and crossed the club building on our right and then turned left to reach the tee box of the first hole. I noticed Jay always walked with long strides, very calm but really brisk. His back was always straight, his shoulders pulled back, and head held high. His overall appearance radiated energy and happiness. I was amazed at his fitness levels; he was about twenty years older than me but had the vigour and motivation of a teenager.

'Harry, I start early in the mornings on weekends when there is hardly anyone on the golf course.'

'Why?' I asked.

'So that I can play all by myself,' Jay said while taking the golf bag from me, unzipping the top and taking out the 1-wood.

'Why would you do that? Don't you need someone to play against?' I asked, surprised.

'Unlike most other games, golf is not a duel between opposing parties.'

'How is that?'

'To appreciate the game, you must first understand the scoring system of golf. You see this board here,' he said, pointing to a white plaque just near the first tee area that said 'Hole No. 1, 438 yards, Par 4'.

'I had mentioned to you earlier the first hole is 438 yards long.'

'Yes, that is the distance between the tee area and the putting hole,' I said.

'However, can you guess what "par 4" means?' Jay queried.

'Par means standard or level,' I guessed.

'You are close, Harry. Par is the number of strokes an expert golfer is expected to take to complete an individual hole. You will see that, of the 18 holes on this golf course, most of them are par 4 with a few par 3s and a couple of par 5s. You are expected to complete a par-4 hole in four strokes starting from tee-off, on to the fairway, negotiating the hazards, then to the putting green and finally hitting the ball into the putting hole or cup.

'And in the same way, every golf course also has a par value. The par for the golf course is the total number of strokes an expert golfer requires to complete the full course. Most full-sized, 18-hole golf courses range from par 69 to 74, with par-72 courses being the most common. The Damdama Golf Course is an 18-hole championship course with par 71. So a player is expected to complete the course in a total of 71 shots.

'On this par-71 course, if you take 100 strokes to complete the 18 holes, you are 29 over par; if you are able to complete all holes in 68 strokes, you are 3 under par,' Jay clarified. He turned around and asked, 'Harry, given this scoring method, tell me, how do we decide who is a better player?'

'Clearly, the player who takes the least number of shots to complete a hole or the entire course,' I replied with confidence. I was getting the hang of this game.

'Absolutely, the lower the number of strokes required, the better you are,' Jay replied looking pleased. 'Now, I have a question for you—since the par number is defined before you start every hole, who are you competing with?'

'I would be competing against an opponent to beat him,' I said, with certainty.

'Think again. What is your real objective?' Jay asked.

'To complete the hole with the least number of strokes,' I said.

'Yes, Harry, but who decides whether you did a good job or not...?'

'Ah!' I said as realisation dawned on me. 'The par value decides whether I did a good job or not!'

'Perfect! You have just discovered the heart of this game—and the crux of life as well. *You are only competing with yourself, even when you think you have an opponent.* Samuel Jackson Snead, a.k.a. Sam Snead, an American professional golfer, always said, *'Forget your opponents; always play against par.'* And probably that attitude made him a giant in golfing history. He holds the record for the maximum number of Professional Golfers'

Association Tour victories and the record for the oldest player to win a PGA Tour at the age of fifty-two in 1965.'

'Wow!' I exclaimed.

'Let's get started with the game, Harry.' Jay moved to the tee area. I stood on the side and saw Jay go through a very conscious, step-by-step and well-practiced process to prepare for the tee-off.

There was silence. He seemed to be in a meditative mode, very mindful and conscious of what he was doing.

Then, with his eyes focused on the ball, he swung the club back in one fluid movement and brought it down, hitting the ball and completing the follow-through. He then lifted his head to see where the ball was going. The ball took off with a 'zing' sound, like a rocket, and landed on the fairway just where the fairway bent towards the left. Jay looked pleased with himself.

'Another shot from there and we should be near the putting green and then with a maximum of 2 shots, the hole will be done. I think I will par this hole, that is, complete this par 4 hole in 4 strokes,' Jay announced.

'It was a beautiful shot, Jay. Looked effortless, but given the distance you have covered, I know it packed a lot of power.' I was awestruck.

Jay bowed and smiled. And then he took out a small towel from the bag, cleaned the driver, and placed it back in the bag. He now started walking towards the fairway, where the ball had landed. I followed him with the trolley.

I wanted to know more about the game and continued with my query. 'So we don't have any outright competition in golf?'

'No, we do have competition in golf, but it is not a duel. All the players play with their own balls. You never tackle, engage, block or confront the opponent like you do in other games. It is not a battle to beat the other person. The objective is to perform better than the other player. You see the difference, Harry?'

'That's an interesting way to look at things. However, that is not how things work in real life. In real life, we have to surpass others in order to succeed. If someone else wins, then I lose. If my competitor gets business from a client, I lose that opportunity,' I countered.

'Harry, you make a good point, and I will come to it in a moment. But staying with golf, remember you have no control over how the other person plays. A player goes around playing their best with their own ball, but they are not shooting at you or challenging you at every shot, unlike tennis, cricket or football. Golf is the only game in which players do not even play the same ball. In golf, you are the whole and sole master of your own destiny.'

'But then, how do you decide who beats whom?' I probed.

'You insist on using the word "beat" but in golf,' Jay explained, 'we would say "win". It is important to note the difference, Harry. You win by becoming better at your own game, not by beating your opponent. *Winners do not beat others, they become better at their own game!*'

'Winning versus beating...'

Jay chuckled at my perplexity.

A Scramble, but Not Quite

'Coming to winning, at professional levels, top players go around playing the course and the one who completes it in the least number of shots, wins. At the club level, you have a number of interesting formats where teams compete with each other, but one of the most unique formats, which is practically impossible in any other sport, is called "scramble". It is probably the only form of competitive sport where people of different skills or different levels of skills can play together. And scramble proves golf is not a purely competitive sport.'

'How is that played?'

'The scramble features teams of four players each. All the players of each team start by hitting from the tee box; then, the team members choose the best of the four shots for the next shot. The other three players then pick up their golf balls and place them next to the ball that was considered to be the best shot. They all play the second shot from there. Play continues in this manner, choosing the best shot to proceed at each step, until the hole and the course is completed. The team with the least number of shots played to complete all holes wins.

'Forming teams in groups of four increases the odds of at least one player on the team hitting a high-quality shot during every rotation, thus helping the entire team move forward from the best spot. A four-person scramble gives each player a chance to shine on various shots on any given hole.

'The role of a leader, whether in the professional world or in personal life, is similar to running a four-person scramble team. You have to lead people with different skills together. You have to ensure each one of them remains engaged. You can't hit all the shots yourself; there are others who will perform based on their own specialisations. Allow them to perform. You have to plan how they can complement each other to achieve your ultimate objective. Right, Harry?'

'Hmm... indeed,' I said, mulling over Jay's latest words of wisdom.

From a Shark to a Dolphin

'In scramble, your ability to collaborate is bigger than your ability to compete. In fact, sustainable and holistic success can only be achieved when everyone participates and everyone wins.

'As you keep rising from a struggler to a winner, you gradually transform from a shark to dolphin,' Jay said as he stopped walking.

He looked at me knowing I will need more explanation.

'A shark to a dolphin? That's an interesting way to look at it,' I said, breaking into a smile.

'Cold-blooded sharks can kill and hunt but they can never build communities. They compete ruthlessly and, therefore, always remain loners. It is believed that sharks have no real social structure other than the survival of the fittest. Even their offspring have to take care of themselves as soon as they are born.

'Warm-blooded mammals, dolphins, by contrast, live in large herds. They are extremely social creatures. They communicate with each other and collaborate for hunting and defending their herd.

'For this reason, good organisations are wary of promoting sharks beyond certain levels of hierarchy because they are acutely aware of the damage such aggressive personalities can wreck on the morale of their people. Mature organisations are always on a lookout for dolphins that can build a collaborative workplace, create room for everyone and in turn allow the organisation to grow as well. Good organisations are able to identify the dolphins early on and, sometimes without any announcements, such professionals find themselves on the fast track. Others wonder why an average performer, who just about met his business objectives, got promoted while someone who was a star performer was not.'

I nodded in agreement.

'A classic example of a dolphin rising to the top is Sundar Pichai,' Jay said. 'No one had heard his name until the founder of Google chose him to take over the top position. Sundar Pichai was named CEO of Google in 2015 and then the CEO of Alphabet, the holding company of Google, in 2019. This is not an ordinary responsibility, given that the market capitalisation of Alphabet is over a trillion dollars.

'And just to put things in perspective, this is one-third the gross domestic product of the entire country of India—even though this is not a fair comparison.'

'Yes, his rise has been phenomenal,' I said.

'Now, there was another capable and more high-profile candidate for this position including their head of business operations and one of the highest-paid Googlers at that time.'

'Yes, who left Google immediately when Sundar Pichai took over,' I added.

'Exactly. It was widely anticipated that this person would take the helm from the founders. This guy was known as an ace dealmaker and a rainmaker for the company but unfortunately, he also had a reputation of being brash and abrasive. People who have worked in Google have reported that this person intentionally made others feel uncomfortable in his presence. His comments and responses would make it very clear that he was the smartest person in the room and he knew it. His body language conveyed superiority and dominance. He was impressive but not pleasant. He was sharp but aggressive like a shark.

'Sundar Pichai, by contrast, maintained a low profile, never trying to steal the limelight. In meetings he would let everyone express their opinions before he gave his own. He was not naïve, but he would advance his agenda through quiet advocacy rather than pushing and hustling others. Google had politics like any other large company, and Sundar navigated those politics to make his team successful while inflicting the least possible damage on any other team.'

'Wow, he could make his team look better without inflicting damage on others... how does one do that?' I wondered out loud.

'Becoming better than others, not beating others. Winners don't beat, they become better. The rise of Sundar Pichai proves that in the high-stakes world, *dolphins win while sharks struggle,*' Jay said.

'Eventually I think competition does bring out the best in people but unbridled competitiveness and aggression destroy the fabric of life. Golf teaches us that progress can be made by competing against ourselves, not by beating others. Our own attitudes and mindsets, not that of others, are more likely to hold us back.'

After walking for a few minutes, we reached the ball that was lying squarely in the middle of the fairway. A large sandpit was on our right-hand side while there were some trees on the other side of the fairway—exactly as I had seen on the map of the first hole while having tea with Jay. A little deviation in the direction of the shot would have landed the ball in one of those hazards. The putting green, or the target, was now visible on the other side. Jay took hold of the bag, and this time he took out an iron to hit the ball further on.

Before he could prepare for the shot, I pressed on with my question.

'So competition is generally bad?'

Jay was swinging the iron and practising his shot but stopped to clarify. 'Competition is not bad. It is the foundation of progress. If people do not compete, we will not push the boundaries of research and development. If countries do not compete, we will not work towards the progress of our people. If we eliminate competition, we will stagnate.

'Golf has competition. At the end of the tournament, the player who completed the course with the fewest strokes wins. But competition on the golf course has a subtle message for us.'

'And what is that?'

'*Competition is good, but don't compete against the wrong person.* Look in the mirror—that's your only competition.'

Be Your Own Cheerleader

'But why do we instinctively compete or compare ourselves with others? What motivates or drives such behaviour?'

'Well, psychologists have proposed that there are two types of motivation that drive people. The first is external motivation that is driven by external rewards such as money, fame, grades, and praise. It is driven by what people see on the outside, and your key driver is: "What will people think?" The second is internal motivation that occurs when we act without any obvious external rewards. We simply enjoy an activity or see it as an opportunity to explore, learn, and actualise our potentials. This is not driven by what people think or what people expect.

'The entire education system, in which we spend our first twenty to twenty-five years of life, programmes us for external motivation—smiley faces on notebooks from the teacher, better marks than others, fear of examination results, praise or punishment from parents, getting selected in competitive examinations, fear of elimination at job interviews, and so on.

'Very soon we are in the real world and get engrossed in chasing success—the way it has been defined by everyone else. Get a job, earn good money, buy a car, get married, buy a home, travel to fancy destinations, chase bigger designations, become rich and famous, and the list just goes on. This pursuit is all-engrossing. The goals and benchmarks are set by others; they are out there in the open, they are very visible and it is therefore natural for us to focus on these goals.'

Jay was keen to make this point very clear to me. So he walked off from the shot and asked for my diary while handing over the iron to me. He flipped a few pages of the diary and showed me the list of life goals I had prepared. 'See, all the goals at the top of your list are driven by external motivation—money, property, car, fame, designation. These are all influenced by comparison with others—comparison with people who have more material possessions than you. These external motivations will make you compete with others. Correct?'

He then drew a little circle and wrote down the external motivators outside the circle and internal motivators inside.

'The circle represents you. All your motivations that will make you a competitor and a fighter are outside the circle. As long as you are outside the circle, you continue to compete and struggle. External motivations drive you into a rat race. It is often difficult to quit the rat race and assess what could be achieved inside the circle. Hence, a large majority of people never graduate beyond the externally placed goals. And do you know the worst part of being externally motivated? You never appreciate what you have. Instead, you focus on what you lack. You end up comparing yourself to others, especially those who have more than you—a sure-shot recipe for unhappiness, isn't it?' Jay concluded.

'So what is the way out?'

'I think golf has an answer for this,' Jay declared. 'Look inside the circle. These are internal motivators. These do not push you to compete with others; rather they make you compete with your own self—to make you feel fulfilled. Exactly like golf, which makes people think about setting goals for themselves that may be very different from what others have set for them. Yet, players with different goals could be playing together at the same time. For example, my goal could be to beat my previous record of 96 strokes whereas my opponent who is a much better player may be trying to go sub-par. Golf has a beautiful scoring system where people of different capabilities can play together. Their scores at the end of the game are adjusted to come to normalised scores. If the better player performed worse than what was expected of him, he may actually lose the game to a player who is less capable than him.'

'Very interesting,' I noted.

'So, even though I am competing against an opponent, I am actually competing only against myself,' Jay explained. 'Golf teaches us to introspect, assess our own capabilities, improve our skills, reflect on our own actions, set our internal benchmarks and goals and become self-motivated. In short, strive for excellence.

'The operating term is *excellence*.' In golf there is no one running past you, hitting at you or throwing anything at you to propel you into action and pushing you to better them or beat them. *Winners are driven by excellence, not external motivations.*

'In life, when you graduate beyond competing with others, you set your own goals that give you a sense of purpose and achievement, happiness and fulfilment. These goals may be very personal, like learning to paint, take photographs, cooking, write a book, or to become physically fit. Or these goals could be professional, where you try to further hone your technical or soft skills to unfurl your true potential.'

Showing me the circle again, he said, 'Let's see, one of your goals is to buy a BMW.'

'Yes, that's been my childhood dream,' I acknowledged.

'So let's assume you save enough money for a down payment

and get to buy one next year. The achievement of this goal will give you immense pleasure. You will throw a party to celebrate the acquisition, people far and wide will find out about your car and congratulate you, and you will even take some people for a spin in your car. Six months later it would have become a part of your lifestyle.

'Now imagine one day a friend calls you to announce he has bought a bigger BMW, a five-series, and is throwing a party to celebrate his purchase. You will visit his house, congratulate him and go for a ride in his new car. The more spacious and luxurious five-series now catches your imagination. The pleasure of owning a BMW is now substantially worn out. Somewhere deep inside, you will be setting a new goal for yourself—your next car will be a bigger BMW. Every time you sit inside your three-series BMW you are reminded of your new goal. Your focus has shifted from ownership to lack of ownership. From pleasure you are now besotted with envy.

'Wouldn't this happen, Harry? Forget cars, it can happen for the new model of an iPhone your friend bought or a camera your colleague got as a birthday present. Your goals are being set by someone other than you. You are simply on a wild goose chase—always a step behind.'

I couldn't disagree with Jay.

'The day you stop competing with others is the day you win the race!'

He was absolutely correct.

Jay seemed pleased with his explanation. He took the golf club back from me and went back for the shot.

There was silence as he adjusted his feet and body and

meditated on the direction and distance of the space ahead of him. There was a small lake, about a hundred yards ahead of us, on the way to the putting green. I guessed his objective was to fly the ball above the lake to the other side. That would be a good achievement.

I heard the crisp sound of the club hitting the ball and saw the ball land far ahead on the other side of the lake.

Another great shot but Jay did not show any emotion. He put the iron back in the bag and we started moving towards the ball.

'So my question remains. What's the way out? I have to live in this society where comparisons are natural. How do I break free from this rat race, Jay?'

'Sure, Harry, you cannot live like an ascetic within the society. You have to maintain certain acceptable standards—just like you have to somehow compete with others when you are in a golf tournament. You cannot avoid it. But internally oriented goals help you rise above the comparison-driven pressures. Establish goals for yourself that are not related to others at all—just like how every golfer sets up a goal to complete the course in fewer strokes than his previous attempt.

'These goals, as I said earlier, can be goals linked to development of skills, self-improvement, helping others—where you are not seeking external validation or approval.

'My wife runs a small charity from home where she and a few other ladies collect money every month, buy food, clothes, books or other basic necessities for orphanages and schools for the underprivileged. Every month they go to different schools and deliver these packets. She measures her success by the joy these gifts bring to the young children. This activity is done quietly, without seeking any publicity or appreciation from the society. Every month she starts with a goal and its achievement gives her immense satisfaction. She is internally motivated. Satisfaction leads to more motivation, which in turn leads to greater effort—a virtuous cycle.'

I was getting the hang of it and remembered some of my life goals. I had some goals of self-improvement but I was convinced I needed more goals that are internally oriented, my very personal goals.

Displaying his mind-reading skills again, Jay said, 'I know you have some self-improvement goals in your list. Bring them to the top of your list. If physical fitness is one of your goals, then you know that sleeping for seven hours every night is important for that. Start keeping a record of your sleeping hours. This will create self-motivation that will help you to avoid late nights. The external motivation may still pull you to show up at a social gathering but your internal motivation will push you to leave the party at the first given opportunity!'

I appreciated Jay's suggestion, but what if my mind was conflicted between internal and external motivation?

Without missing a beat, Jay said, 'And you know what, the reward systems of the two motivations are very different. When you act based on external motivation, you get the reward of external approval. The gratification is instantaneous but the loss of pleasure can also be instantaneous—for example, your friend bought a more expensive car or, god forbid, someone on the street puts a scratch on your shining car. Imagine!'

I flinched just imagining that scenario. Jay was right.

'But when you act based on your internal motivations, the rewards are also internal. No one is going to acknowledge your success. Only you will experience it. The reward may come late—for example, trying to get seven hours of sleep may require a major overhaul of your daily routine including some difficult adjustments like avoiding coffee during the day and hitting the bed by 10 p.m. That means a "no" to socialising regularly and a "no" to binge-watching television. But after a couple of weeks, once you start seeing the rewards of waking up in the morning as fresh as a baby, experiencing that extra bounce in your steps and a sense of calm and stability through the day, you will frown upon external motivations for evening parties, late nights, pointless socialising and latest television shows. *Internal motivations lead you to richer and longer-lasting rewards.*

There's Always More Pie

I had a lot going through my mind, but my biggest concern remained how to manage the problems in my office. How do I position myself for the next promotion? How should I manage competition from the other VPs in the company? So I asked Jay, 'You spoke about healthy competition—competing and collaborating. I liked that idea. But how can I collaborate with competing firms for business in the market or the other VPs in my company when basically I am competing with all of them?'

'Thank you, Harry. You have raised a very important point. How do you compete yet collaborate? It is entirely possible, and the good news is if you are successful at this rare skill, you will position yourself as the absolute leader. Your business offers software solutions to customers. Correct?'

'Yes, we offer software solutions to banks and financial-services firms to manage end-to-end processes. And now we are rolling out our cloud-based solution that will dramatically cut down the capital expenditure and operational manpower required by these companies, making them superefficient. In fact, we are by far the leaders in this field, but lately, many smaller competitors have crept in and are undercutting us in price,' I said, describing my company's business.

'Are all the financial-services companies using some sort of software or cloud-based solutions like yours?'

'Some are, but many are still using outdated systems or home-grown patchy solutions.'

'So, your system is something that they would all benefit from?'

'Definitely, they will benefit immensely from our systems, Jay.'

'Then why do you have a scarcity mindset?' Jay asked.

'What is a "scarcity mindset"?' I was intrigued. Jay always brought up concepts I had never heard of.

'Each competitor in your industry, including you, is fighting with each other as though one company's profit is the other company's loss. Your thinking implies there are only so many customers in the country and customers should be divided up like slices of a pie. When you think there is only a finite amount of success available in this world, you fall into the scarcity mindset. You think the pie is finite. You want to grab a slice for yourself.

'The scarcity mindset is a self-limiting belief that prevents you from winning big.'

I did always look at the pie and try to maximise my share of it. For years, that is how we have been drawing the marketplace in our business presentations.

'Now think about this, Harry. What if the companies that use your cloud-based solution become so amazingly efficient and profitable that other businesses start following suit? Maybe five businesses may draw inspiration from the first one and another five from each of those five. Whether you sold the solution or your competitor, the result is that the pie grows and even if your market share remains the same, you have a bigger slice to eat—isn't it?'

Since I looked a bit puzzled, Jay took the diary from me and drew an illustration of two pies:

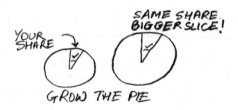

'Focus on growing the pie, not grabbing a slice. So everyone wins.'

'This is a new way of looking at things. Frankly, I never thought of this,' I said, impressed with Jay's perspective.

'So the question that arises, Harry, is how can you implement this abundance mindset in practice?'

'How?' I asked.

'The answer lies in something called "co-opetition",' Jay announced.

'I have never heard this term. What does it mean?'

'Co-opetition is a word that combines cooperation and competition. When you can cooperate with your competitors for mutual benefits, you achieve co-opetition,' Jay explained. 'In fact, this is a concept I learnt from a samosa seller near my house and also from my son.'

'Oh?'

'A samosa shop in the office complex near our house has a roaring business. The seller opens his little stall only for a couple of hours in the morning when people looking for breakfast crowd around him to buy fresh, deep-fried samosas. Next to him is a tea seller whose stall is open throughout the day. But his business picks up significantly during the few hours when people are buying samosas from his neighbouring stall.

'One day I had a brainwave to help my friendly samosa seller. I highlighted to him that his business was a significant driver for the tea stall and that he was just giving away what could be his. He looked a bit puzzled and asked me to explain.

'Like a good consultant I presented my business idea that could further increase his revenues. I suggested that if he started boiling some tea within his own stall, he could double his business. After all, everyone enjoyed his samosas while sipping piping hot and sugary masala tea from his neighbour's stall.

'And, you know what, he turned around and said, "Sir, that will be very easy for me but do you know half of my customers are originally his customers who enjoy a samosa along with their tea. You can see how many of them are buying from here and standing and chatting up with him. And the other half is my customer base. They stand here and chit-chat with me while ordering tea from his stall. Each one of us is growing the overall business potential of this area. Why would I reduce my business by eliminating him? *I give so that I can get!*" I was shocked to listen to this simple but profound wisdom. I thought I had a great business mind,' Jay said with a snort, 'but the humble samosa seller turned out to be a guru of business management. He is a true winner.'

Incredible. This samosa seller was growing the pie rather than grabbing a slice of it. He embodied the abundance mindset that Jay had just spoken about.

'And how did you learn from your son?' I asked.

'Ah, that was another good lesson for me. In school some of my son's classmates were not so good at studies. So on weekends, after completing his own studies and assignments, my son would take classes for his classmates and help them cover the portion that was taught in school during the previous week.

'Now, these classmates were his competitors. He wanted to top his class, and by helping these students he was actually increasing competition for himself.

'When I asked him about this strange arrangement, his answer surprised me. He said, "Dad, by teaching I am only revising and strengthening my own concepts. It is a win-win—my classmates will improve but I will excel."

'These lessons taught me the concept of winning by coopetition. *Winners focus on giving rather than grabbing.* Giving increases the size of the pie and everyone benefits, including the giver.

'To really appreciate this concept, you have to start by placing all competition in perspective, whether external or internal. I know it is difficult in the beginning, but try to rise above the warzone and see the big picture. Who is your real competition—your colleague running another branch of your company or your competition outside the company? While evaluating your external competitors, try to see who your real competition is—another company or an outdated substitute product? Try to find opportunities to partner with your so-called competitors.'

'And how do I grow the pie for my business?' I asked.

'Find opportunities to work together, give out and grow the pie. Collaborate with other area heads to evolve a national strategy to increase business. You do not always need your boss to do this. You guys can sit down together and brainstorm, and you could take the lead. Reach out to your competitors in the marketplace and call them for a seminar to increase awareness of the new cloud-based solutions. Get together with your competitors and organise public awareness sessions on your solutions. This will help the financial-services industry become more efficient and profitable. The growing pie has enough for everyone.

'But, to begin with, you have to give rather than grab. Give your time to others and listen to them; motivate them and promote them; freely share your ideas for growth with others and coach them to achieve their true potential—yes, even if they are your competitors! Why? Because they will all work towards growing the pie.

'And that for you, Harry, is co-opetition in practice. These are some of the ways you cooperate or collaborate with your competitors and benefit personally.

'When you start co-opeting with your colleagues and industry competitors, you will always be a winner. The best-case scenario is that you will collectively grow your business and become more successful in your career. The base-case scenario is that you will at least position yourself as a leader in your company and in your industry. It is a win-win situation for you,' Jay declared.

'The moment you start living with an abundance mindset, start giving freely, stop thinking about surpassing others and stop mindlessly competing to get ahead is the day you become a winner.

'Lao Tzu, the ancient Chinese philosopher, while describing a formidable leader said, *"Because a winner competes with no one, no one can compete with him."* This is the real secret of winning a game, long before you even start playing, isn't it?'

'I must admit, Jay, as you were talking about mindlessly competing with others, I had a flashback in my mind. I always blamed my boss for my stagnating career, but I was completely unaware of my own limiting beliefs about business. In my urge to overtake the others in my company, I positioned myself as a warrior and an aggressive shark. I was trying to grab a bigger slice of the pie from others but had never thought about growing the pie. I was trying to pull others down and hoping my seniors would consider me a suitable candidate to lead everyone. I had never imagined giving anything to anyone—not even a kind word, let alone a sales lead that did not belong to my territory. I had been fighting with my competitors and crushing them, without understanding the value they could bring to me in the long run,' I said, sharing my new-found awareness

'Go on, I am listening,' Jay said encouragingly, knowing that I had not finished yet.

'You know about the Super Financial order that I secured for my branch?'

'Yes, I know all about it,' Jay said with a knowing look.

'Instead of poaching the client that actually belonged to the Bangalore region, if I had passed on the sales lead to my colleagues in Bangalore, I could have positioned myself as a leader in the organisation. I would have lost the order for my branch but would have earned the respect of all my colleagues and seniors. That would have paved the path to my promotion.'

I could see Jay break into a big smile.

'Thank you, Jay. You just taught me another million-dollar lesson,' I said, with sincere gratitude, while turning a page in my diary to make some more notes.

Mindset 4: Excellence
Stop Racing, Start Winning

Winners do not try to beat others; they become better at their own game. Winners give rather than grab.

Take a shot:
Think about your deepest drivers and motivations—are they external or internal? Don't set your goals based on comparisons with others.

How often do you give, rather than grab? Can you try to help, motivate and promote others around you and experience the success it brings to your life? How can you grow the pie—at work, in life and in relationships?

No More Puttering Around

We walked past the lake and on the fairway towards the ball, which had landed quite close to the green. There was still a little distance between where the ball had landed and the periphery of the green. A flagstick was pinned in the hole in the middle of the green, which I guess was to make it easy for the player to take aim.

'You play well, Jay. In 2 shots, you are near the green, and in the next shot you will putt the ball,' I said, sounding like an experienced coach.

'Not yet. It will take me a shot to land the ball onto the green, close to the putting hole and then another shot to putt the ball. The game now becomes tricky.'

'Why?' I asked.

'When you are so close to the hole, you end up making more mistakes than usual,' Jay replied.

'I would have imagined this is the easiest part. You've hit the really long and difficult shots and covered the entire fairway to reach this final section.'

'Harry, the skills required at this distance are quite distinct.'

'I guess the skills remain the same, but maybe you do not need as much strength?' I suggested.

'Not really. When you are teeing off, you want the ball to cover as much distance as possible. Accuracy of direction is important, but only to the extent that the ball lands on the fairway. The distance to be covered is more important.

'Near or on the putting green, both the speed of the ball and accuracy of direction become critical. Short-range execution skills are very different from the long-range teeing off skills.'

'Can you explain?' I requested.

'If I hit the ball too hard, it will overshoot, and if I am too soft, it will not reach the hole at all. The ball is tiny and the hole is small, just 4.25 inches in diameter. Therefore, the speed and direction, both are important to ensure the ball does not miss the hole.'

'It is quite funny, Jay. Isn't the golf hole too small? You play on a course where every stretch is many hundred metres long but the final goal is tiny by comparison,' I remarked.

'Yes, it is tiny and that makes playing golf even more difficult. The long hits are easier but the short ones are difficult. This is just like life, isn't it? It is sometimes easier to make big, bold plans but many fail because execution of the small details gets muddled up. *Execution trumps vision!*

'Well, on the golf course, executing the putting shot is made easier by marking the holes with a tall flagstick. Players can view the hole from a distance and aim towards it. The flagstick is removed when you are on the putting green, attempting to send the ball into the hole.'

Thoughts Become Things

As we were talking, Jay was getting ready for the next shot, from just outside the putting green. He inspected the area and then gave his assessment. 'This area is quite uneven. If I had been on the putting green, I could have simply rolled the ball into the hole. But from here I will have to hit the ball in the air, at a trajectory, so that it lands as close to the hole as possible, maybe with one bounce.

'By the way, this is called a pitch shot. It will not carry the ball very far but will lift it in the air. The ball will have a steep ascent and an equally steep descent, avoiding the unevenness of the territory in the middle.'

And then, pointing towards his golf bag, he asked, 'Can you find the nine-iron for me? These high-numbered irons are called wedges.'

I opened Jay's golf bag and found a narrow clubhead that had a big '9' engraved on it. It was shorter than the other irons and its face was at a steep angle. I pulled it out and handed it over to Jay.

Jay steadied his stance, took aim, shifted his feet to align them and adjusted the direction of the shot carefully. I observed the imaginary line joining the tips of his shoes was pointing towards the hole. He bent his knees a bit, followed his pre-shot rituals and, then with a smooth swing, hit the ball. The ball went high up and then landed softly, on line and close to the hole.

'I noticed your swing was not the kind of full swing that you had taken in the long shots,' I said, pleased with my observation.

'You are correct, Harry. The swing was about three-quarters of a normal swing because I am not trying to cover a lot of distance. A full swing with a lofted club would simply hit the ball higher and increase the chance of missing the direction.'

'And now, can I have my putter?' Jay asked, handing over the iron back to me.

'Sure.'

I placed the club back into the bag and pulled out the putter for him. The putter was really short compared to the other clubs.

Jay noticed I was trying to figure out why the putter was so different from the other clubs.

'Harry, a putter is used to make low-speed strokes with the intention of rolling the ball into the hole from a short distance.

'The putting stroke is a straight shot. The putting action does not require a swing. It is merely a push. You do not want your wrist to move.'

'Okay, that sounds logical. Let me see how you play the putting stroke,' I said.

'Taking aim is the key to a successful putt. I like to walk from the ball to the hole to get a better idea of the green and then walk back to the ball. I then squat down to see its best route to the hole. On a flat-surface green, I will take a straight route, but on an inclined green like this one, I will aim the ball a little to the side of the hole. This is because I know gravity will move the ball slightly to the right as it rolls over from here to the hole. The important skill here is to visualise the putt:

122

mentally draw a line tracing the path you intend the ball to take.

'The long game requires strategy and vision while the short game requires careful execution. A small one percent deviation by the putter can lead to the ball missing the hole by a couple of feet. Just like life. *Winning the game of life requires one percent vision and ninety-nine percent execution.*'

Jay made a gesture with his right arm, mentally measuring the distance from his right eye to the hole while I listened intently.

'The more detailed the visualisation, the better, so do not be afraid to close your eyes and really use your imagination to create an image of the shot in your mind.

'In fact, Jack Nicklaus, the legendary golf champion, propagated this concept, which has now become a standard practice for winning golfers. He said he never hits a shot, even in practice, before having a sharp, in-focus picture of it in his mind. He would imagine its path, trajectory and even its behaviour on landing.

'By visualising and meditating on a plan, your brain uses specific neural pathways to send impulses to the specific motor nerves and muscles to execute the plan. When you are visualising, you are telling the brain which pathways it needs to use,' Jay explained.

'Does it work?' I wanted to know.

Jay smiled. 'You know what, it does. Your thoughts become things. *What you can visualise, you can materialise!*'

'But what should I visualise to achieve my goals?' I asked.

'Visualise your success often, like becoming a well-respected industry leader, becoming a famous author, spending time with your wife or playing with your children and enjoying those precious moments. Your powerful subconscious can translate your visualisation into intentions that finally become actions. What you speak and what you do then just guide you *magically* to your goals,' Jay said.

He then paused for a deep breath and said, 'The trick is to visualise the achievement of your goal. Visualise and feel as if you have already achieved your big goal. Feel the joy and happiness of achievement and do not harbour an iota of doubt in your mind. Creative visualisation is not day dreaming. It is a more emotional exercise—you actually get into the scene and start imagining how you look, what you say and discuss, how you conduct yourself, how others react, what your feelings and thoughts are.'

'Hmm... I think I'll try this technique, Jay.'

'It is easy to use, Harry,' Jay assured me. 'You know what, I told you about my bakery friend who sticks pictures of exotic holiday destination for his team to hit the profit numbers? What is he doing? The same thing—he wants his team to visualise their achievement. They see the beautiful pictures every day and want to be there. They start experiencing the joy and happiness of walking in those picturesque locations. Unknown to them, in the background, the brain gradually starts programming the neuron paths required to take them there, giving them the motivation and drive to work towards the profit numbers.'

'This is a very smart idea, Jay,' I acknowledged.

'Now, Harry, can you please go there and pull the flagstick out and hold it just behind the hole?' Jay requested.

I did as instructed.

The Long and Short of the Game

Jay had taken position for the putt. His stance was quite similar to the other shots. He explained, 'See, my elbows are dug into the body so that the movement of my arms does not deviate from the line I am aiming at.'

Then he became quiet as though becoming fully mindful of the ball and the path ahead. He moved the putter in a pendulum motion in the air a couple of times, just to align with the intended direction, and then gently hit the ball. The ball started rolling up on one side of the hole and then, just as he had predicted, under the effect of gravity, it straightened up towards the hole. It looked like a perfect shot, neither too hard nor too soft. The ball had just enough momentum to carry it to the hole. And just as I was about to congratulate Jay, the ball suddenly stopped, about two inches short of the hole, where I was standing.

'Oh!' I exclaimed.

'Doesn't matter, Harry. It is just a game, and I tried my best. Yes, putting can be the most frustrating shot in the game. It looks so easy, yet it is so difficult.'

Jay moved forward and then once again, took aim. With an even more relaxed stance this time, he carefully and gently stroked the ball into the hole.

'Excellent, you still did well. You completed this par-4 hole in 5 strokes,' I beamed.

'Yes, that's not bad but I could have done better. Anyway, this is history now. But you just got a demonstration of how difficult the short game, or execution, can be.' He laughed and retrieved the ball from the cup inside the hole.

I planted the flagstick back into the hole while Jay took out the score card from his bag and noted down the number of shots he took for the first hole. He handed it over to me, gesturing that I should note down the score for the next holes and then started walking towards the next tee area.

'You were right when you said putting is trickier than the long shots,' I remarked.

'Putting is a skill that distinguishes good players from the excellent ones. Many players do not realise that putting is half the game,' Jay explained.

'But putting is only at the end of every hole... so, how is it half the game?' I asked, surprised.

'We did discuss this sometime ago, remember? The par value for each hole always consists of 2 putts and the number of strokes it should take to reach the green. So, on a par 4, an expert golfer is expected to need only 2 strokes to reach the putting green, followed by 2 putting strokes to putt the ball in the hole. On a par 5, 3 strokes to the green and then 2 putting strokes. Since there are 18 holes, we have 36 putting strokes. And given that the average course is a par 72 or 71, this means half the game is played only on the putting green.

'Average golfers spend too much time practising their long game at the expense of their wedge and putter play. The driving range, where we were at the start, is always filled with golfers banging away on their drivers. You will hardly see anyone practising the putting shot even though that can be practised practically anywhere, including in your living room, and that can dramatically improve your score.'

'Oh, my CEO has a mini putting range in his office!' I said remembering what I had seen in the head office.

'He has figured out that the short game is a low-hanging fruit of golf. It is where you can improve your scores with the lowest time investment. Bobby Locke, a famous South African professional golfer, would say, "You drive for show, but putt for dough".'

I laughed. 'So, he means the long and dramatic driving shots give you the pleasure and publicity, but it is the small and boring putting shots that actually earn you money, your dough?'

'That's right, my boy! You're catching on quick!' said Jay, lightly patting my shoulder to show his appreciation.

Who Will Bell the Cat?

We were now on the next hole, and Jay was looking around and preparing for the tee shot. As I was taking the wood out of the golf bag for him, he stood still for a while. Then he looked at me and said, 'Life is all about getting both the long game and the short game right. You remember we talked about goal setting?'

'Yes, I do.'

'Big strategic goals in your life are your long game. Breaking those big goals into small actionable, tactical plans and executing them is your short game. Like the powerful tee shot, the long game—defining your long-term goals or strategic plan—is ambitious; it allows you to make big statements and think big.'

'Think big,' I interjected, recollecting the motivational quote.

'And hence goal setting is important. If we do not define our life goals, we are likely to be hitting in all directions hoping for a positive outcome—much like throwing darts blindfolded and hoping to hit the bull's eye. It will never happen.

'The day you realise you have been playing blind, you will launch the rest of your life with big, long-term objectives using Warren Buffett's three-step process. After that you will break them down to smaller goals and create the momentum to see them through using the GROW model, where W stands for the Way Forward, or execution.

'And this is where the short game starts. A seasoned golfer knows a good tee shot is just the beginning, and that success is still far away in a small hole a few hundred yards away.

'The short game—short-term planning, lining up the small steps, managing your daily schedule and executing the steps—is where the rubber really hits the road. The short game offers no room for dreaming. Here you require more finesse and accuracy. *Small acts lead to big victories.*'

And then Jay turned around and said, 'Actually, now is a good time to tell you one of my favourite Aesop fables.' Jay cleared his throat before continuing. 'A large group of mice living in a hole was regularly hounded by the house cat. Fed up with the constant threat, one day they held a meeting to figure out how to free themselves of their terrifying enemy. Many ideas were considered and rejected. Finally, when they were about to give up, a young mouse got up and suggested all they have to do is hang a bell around the cat's neck, for when they hear the bell ringing, they will know the cat is coming and they will have time to run away. Everyone agreed this was a marvellous plan and their troubles were over. They started dancing and singing with joy. But in the midst of the celebration, an old mouse sitting in the corner came forward and asked, "I agree... this is a very good plan. Let me ask one question: Who will go and put the bell around the cat's neck—who will bell the cat?"

'The festivities stopped and there was dead silence. No one had thought about that!

'Moral of the story is that thinking big is not enough. We often get carried away by our big ideas and forget that ideas are like commodities—implementation is the key to success.'

Turning towards me, he said. 'The same principle applies in your personal life. One of your life goals that you defined was physical fitness, correct?'

I nodded.

'This is "thinking big"—your big goal. But waking up every day dreaming of this goal will not take you anywhere unless you act on it. How do you start executing this goal?'

'I should break down the goal into smaller goals?' I ventured a guess.

'Absolutely, and each of those smaller goals has to be executed with perfection. If your goal is to change your eating habits, you would probably need to have regular smaller meals rather than irregular larger meals; making time for physical exercise, which would mean creating a regular routine for the day, which in turn could mean regulating your sleeping pattern. Then we can further break each one of them down to steps that involve pure execution—your call to act small. This may require you to completely rejig your lifestyle.'

And then he brought back the analogy of the short game in golf. 'In executing the short-distance strokes in golf, direction is more important than distance. On the putting green, when your ball is lying just ten feet from the hole, your primary focus is on getting the direction right. A one-degree deviation at the point of hitting the ball may lead to the ball missing the hole by one foot.

'Similarly, in executing the small goals, you have to put yourself in the right direction. It is important you start small and stay on course rather than try to achieve your objectives in one shot.

'If you are trying to regulate your sleeping pattern, you cannot achieve the final goal of seven hours of sleep, let us say between 10 p.m. and 5 a.m., in one stroke or one day. You will have to start with small adjustments first—like trying to regulate the pattern over the weekends, when you have more control over your routine. When that stabilises, try another day in the week. As long as you are heading in the right direction, achieving your goal is just a matter of time.'

'That is a very helpful suggestion, Jay. You've simplified a big goal, that looked scary to begin with, into small achievable steps!'

The Nitty-Gritty of Execution

As I chewed over all these ideas, I realised something. 'Jay, if I start breaking down my big goals, they will all boil down to time management. How can I manage so many things in a day? Sleep well, work like a dog in the office, spend time with family, look after my physical fitness… there are only twenty-four hours during the day. Execution of my big life goals requires a lot of small activities. Where is the time?'

It was as if Jay was waiting for this question. 'Aha! Here I take help from a US president.'

Jay had this know-it-all look on his face and I could not help but laugh. 'A US president? What has that got to do with me making more time in a day?'

He pointed at the diary he had given me. 'Show me your diary.'

I handed over the diary and pen to Jay, knowing fully well that an illustration was in store for me. This time, he drew a box and divided it into four quadrants.

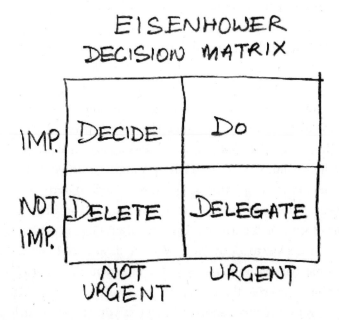

He then explained what he had drawn: 'This is called the Eisenhower Decision Matrix, named after the thirty-fourth American president, Dwight D. Eisenhower. He is supposed to be the guru of time management, task management, and productivity and this box has been derived from his famous quote: *I have two types of problems, the urgent and the important. The urgent are not important and the important are never urgent.'*

Jay realised I didn't quite understand the difference so he clarified further. 'Important tasks are the ones that help us in achieving our own goals, and often come without deadlines. Urgent tasks usually help others in achieving their goals, but often come with deadlines. Hence, the urgent tasks end up taking up most of our time.

'This tool helps you prioritise your efforts and maximise your productivity, exactly how Eisenhower did.

'You know that you will have to immediately work on tasks that are urgent and important like responding to your client's query, your boss's email, a medical emergency at home or a call from your kid's school. You cannot delay such tasks and you cannot delegate them to anyone else. You just *do* these tasks.

'Important but not urgent are tasks, such as daily physical exercise, spending time with family, meeting with your financial planner, learning photography, making a long-term business strategy with your partner, that can wait if you are running short of time on a particular day. Not always but when required, you can decide to delay such tasks or drop a couple of them on some day without any severe consequences. You have the flexibility to *decide* the timing of these tasks.

'Urgent but not important are tasks you can easily delegate to someone else when you are short of time. You may not have many such tasks when you start your day but these tasks crop up during the day. Imagine you are working on compiling the sales data that has to be sent to the head office before noon when an important client calls you for a meeting. You cannot refuse the client nor can you delay the sales report. But you can easily delegate the report work to a capable colleague. When such situations arise, consign them to the *delegate* box and move on.'

'Okay, I can understand the utility of this tool. But what is this last quadrant?' I asked.

'The last quadrant is for tasks that are neither urgent nor important. Normally you should not have anything in this box but if you find yourself involved in tasks that can qualify for this quadrant, *delete* them. The unnecessary robs energy from the important. An example could be checking your phone every ten minutes and responding to texts messages, forwarding interesting content over a messaging app, scrolling through social media posts, attending to the bulk of the emails that really have no purpose, spending time with a colleague who drops by just for a chat or mindlessly sitting in front of the television because you do not feel like doing anything else!

'You can use this matrix for as many aspects of your life as you want,' Jay suggested. 'Next time you are faced with a decision or you are committing your time to any activity, stop and ask yourself, "Am I doing this because it is important or am I doing it because it is merely urgent?"

'The moment you start applying this to your life, Harry, you will suddenly experience an abundance of time with the same twenty-four hours that all of us get every day. Rather than mindlessly rushing from one task to another trying to finish work, take a step back and become aware of the quadrant you are operating in. *Winners organise, not just do.*'

'I like this approach, Jay. I am going to use it on an on-going basis every day to prioritise my efforts and focus only on things that give me the maximum returns on time invested. Thank you indeed for introducing me to this matrix. I promise I will make it my second nature,' I said with sincere gratitude.

Jay was beaming with joy.

I was imagining my life, my work, and my relations, and all of a sudden something did not make sense. Deep in my thoughts, I reached for my diary once again and quickly wrote down the key lessons.

'The game is now becoming interesting. Get ready to face some tough dilemmas,' Jay announced as he started to move.

I knew this was a hint at another life lesson from golf.

Mindset 5: Execution
Think Big but Act Small

Winners focus on small acts that lead to big victories.

Take a shot:
Have you broken down your big goals into smaller actions? Ninety-nine percent of the success comes from careful execution of small steps.

Visualise your success. Visualise, in great detail, how success would look and feel, and let your subconscious mind guide you to your goals.

Do you feel overwhelmed by work? Think about how you can organise your life using the Eisenhower Decision Matrix.

Fairway or the Highway

L ost in these discussions, I did not realise when we had completed a few more holes. Jay was once again moving resolutely towards the next one. I finished writing a few notes, folded my diary, tucked it into the side pocket of Jay's golf bag and hurried to catch up with him.

'I have a question, Jay.'

'Go ahead,' he responded.

'What do you mean by "handicap" in golf?'

Jay seemed happy with my question. 'A golf handicap is a measure of a golfer's ability—actually his potential ability. In the most simplistic terms, the lower the handicap of a player, the better he is relative to those with higher handicaps. It means he has the potential to complete the entire course in fewer shots compared to a player with a higher handicap.

'It is a number that is calculated based on a player's recent score history and is not a fixed number. Players have to keep submitting their score card, as they play, to the golf federation in their city along with details of which golf course they played on, for the calculation of their handicap.'

'That's quite an elaborate method just to get your handicap,' I exclaimed.

'Yes,' said Jay, 'it is because it serves a very important function in the game. The handicap system allows players of varying abilities to play against each other and enjoy the game together. Remember, this is not a game in which you simply try to beat the opponent. It is also a game of enjoying some time with other players in a healthy and fair competition. The operative term is fair competition.'

A Fair Play

'So, to give you a clearer picture of how handicap works, let us take a simple example of two players, Mr A and Mr B, with handicaps of 28 and 10 playing together. First, tell me, who is a better player?'

'The one with the lower handicap, Mr B, by a big margin,' I replied with certainty. After all, the player who takes fewer number of shots to complete the hole is a better player.

'Correct. On a standalone basis, Mr B is far superior to Mr A, but when they play together, a handicap adjustment will have to be applied to make the competition fair.'

'How does that work?' I asked, more curious than ever.

'That's simple. After the game is over, the handicap number of each player is subtracted from their gross scores to arrive at a net score. Let us say in this example, by the end of the game,

Mr A completes the 18 holes of the golf course in 100 strokes while Mr B does it in 89. These are their gross scores. If you do not adjust their handicaps, you will come to the conclusion that Mr B played better since he completed the course using fewer strokes. But that does not give us a fair picture.'

Jay wrote down these scores against the names of the players and then subtracted the handicap number of each to come to a net score:

	A	B	
HANDICAP	28	10	← BETTER HANDICAP
ACTUAL SCORE (SHOTS TAKEN)	100	89	← FEWER SHOTS
NET SCORE	100-28 (=72)	89-10 =79	

BUT WINNER! →

'See, the picture has changed. The net score for Mr A is lower than that of Mr B. So, in reality, Mr A played much better than what was expected of him and won this game!'

'Wow, this is quite unique. I cannot imagine applying such an adjustment in any other game!' I exclaimed.

'Harry, the handicap system of golf scoring has been created to even the playing field, allowing golfers of widely varying talent levels to compete against one another on an equal footing. Golf is a game for winners. Winners are confident of their skills;

they like to win by fair competition, not by taking advantage of others. *Using fair means to win reflects your confidence in your own skills.*'

'Being so fair to the opponent and allowing them an adjustment in scores based on their handicap is just too idealistic. Don't you think so, Jay?' I asked, not convinced.

'That's the beauty of this game, Harry. Why do you think I said golf is not really a competitive sport? You know what, golf is more like a rehearsal for real life on a golf course. Golf brings out the real character of people. Author PG Wodehouse famously said, '*To find a man's true character, play golf with him*', and the Hall of Fame British golfer Percy Boomer said, '*If you wish to hide your character, do not play golf.*'

The Cost of Victory

As we reached the next hole, Jay asked for his driver and prepared himself for the tee-off. He executed an effortless swing and hit the ball. The ball flew away beautifully, but rather than landing on the fairway, it landed inside a sand bunker running parallel to the fairway. Jay smiled and handed back the club to me. By now, I already knew that Jay was meticulous and liked to clean his clubs before putting them back in the case.

I took out the small towel and rubbed the clubhead clean before slipping it back into the bag.

Looking pleased with my action, he beckoned me to follow him as he set out towards the sandpit. The pit was about a foot deep and the ball was near the edge, close to the fairway. Without Jay asking for it, I pulled out the sand wedge and handed it over to him. I guessed it from the SW engraved on the head. He was impressed. 'Aren't I a fast learner,' I thought, pleased at my quick grasp of the game.

Jay carefully stepped into the bunker and positioned himself for the stroke. He then started practising a few swings in the air while straightening his back and loosening his knees. Just when he was about to swing, he stopped and suddenly backed off from the spot.

'What happened?' I asked.

'I will explain—but first, Harry, can you pass me my score card?'

I did not know what had happened but I did as I was told. I saw Jay making a mark under Hole No. 6—where we were playing now.

'Harry, I just incurred a penalty. I broke a rule that says that while in a sand bunker, a player cannot touch the sand with his club before making a stroke. My club grazed the surface of the sand bunker while I was practising my swing in the air. Therefore, I will have to add an extra stroke to my score for this hole.'

'But I did not see your club touching the sand, Jay,' I responded, quite sure he was mistaken.

'Doesn't matter. I know it touched the sand. I felt it. And that is enough,' Jay stated.

'But isn't this a silly rule? How does it matter? Violating this rule does not give you any advantage in the game,' I argued.

'Golf has many peculiar rules, but in this game, the rules are sacrosanct. It is a matter of honour and dignity to follow the rulebook. A winner will lose the game but not his honour. *Integrity is victory!*'

It sounded idealistic but given what I had learnt about golf so far, I was not surprised.

'And what makes this all the more important to golfers is they typically are left to police themselves.'

'Don't you have referees or umpires in golf?' I asked.

'There are no referees or scorekeepers in golf even though golf has the most complex set of rules, which evolved over the last four hundred years or so. This is another part of the golf honour system: each player is responsible for keeping his or her own score, and for doing it fairly and honestly. In major championships, there may be a rules officer nearby for the players to consult and even then—not always with every group of players,' Jay elaborated.

I was surprised. 'Jay, you cannot imagine playing football, cricket, tennis and any other game without referees, umpires or judges. They even have cameras to keep a watch on the players to ensure they stick to the rules!'

'Harry, at the 2001 British Open, Welshman Ian Woosnam was clearly in the lead for a pay cheque of 360,000 pounds and the coveted trophy, the Claret Jug. While teeing for the final round, he suddenly realised he had fifteen clubs in his bag, a violation of Rule Number Four of the Royal and Ancient Golf Club of St Andrews, which restricts the number of clubs to only fourteen. Ian was practising with two drivers before the final round, but this was also his caddy's fault, who should have counted the clubs before coming on the tee.

'Oh my,' I remarked reflexively.

Jay nodded. 'Ian immediately called the match referee and informed him of the breach. He then added 2 strokes to his score. Had he said nothing, nobody would have been ever the wiser. Those 2 extra strokes cost him a lot of money and his lifelong dream of holding the famous Claret Jug! However, it made him immortal in the world of golf, and today he has become the gold standard for integrity on golf circuits.'

'Truly a commendable act,' I said.

'In 1925, at the US Open, American Bobby Jones, one of the finest golfers ever, was deep in the rough; his ball was lying amidst the tall grass. While addressing the ball, his feet pushed the tall grass slightly, which moved the ball a tiny bit. Touching or moving the ball before hitting it is not allowed. He promptly notified his competitor, Walter Hagen, that he was calling a 1-stroke penalty on himself. Walter was not convinced, and the rules officer who questioned others found that no one—Bobby's caddy or the spectators, not even any of the other competitors— had seen the ball move.'

'No way!' I said, impressed with these legendary golfers' display of integrity.

'Both Walter and the officer implored Bobby Jones to reconsider his decision. Bobby would have none of it and ended the game in a tie. In the tie-breaker round, Bobby lost the title by a margin of just one stroke. Bobby's integrity cost him the championship but catapulted him to the stature of a global hero of the game. Later, when he was praised for his honesty, he said, "You might as well praise a man for not robbing a bank."'

'That is real honesty, Jay. Without doubt golf is a game of leaders and winners. Even Walter displayed amazing strength of character by asking Bobby Jones, his opponent, to reconsider his decision. Awesome!' I exclaimed, quite sure that such things existed only in golf.

So far, it had been an interesting day. I had learnt so much about golf and life.

Jay returned to the ball and with the sand wedge, gently lifted the ball out, high enough to escape the edges of the bunker and far enough to land squarely in the middle of the fairway again. After that, he took the rake, evened out the sand surface, and walked out of the sand bunker.

Follow Your Compass

Jay handed back the sand wedge and asked for the three-iron. 'Every day, we see examples of people trying to bend the rules or push the boundaries of ethics to get ahead. In the long run, it does not help,' Jay declared.

While Jay was preparing for the next stroke on the fairway, my mind was telling me that Jay was referring to my style of doing business. I had frequently influenced purchasing managers by offering them complimentary holidays or expensive gifts to secure orders—even though this was strictly against my firm's policy. Maybe Jay had even overheard the conversation about the entertainment I had organised for the management of Super Financials to secure their contract. I couldn't help but retort, 'But there are business pressures that force people to use shortcuts and cheat sometimes. They wouldn't want to do it if there wasn't any pressure to deliver unrealistic targets.'

'Look, Harry, *morality is the difference between becoming successful and staying successful.* Success can be built on shortcuts but unfortunately it does not last,' Jay said seriously. The morning was suddenly beginning to feel uncomfortable.

'By integrity, are you referring to financial honesty?' I asked, echoing the thoughts that had been in my mind about securing orders in return for financial favours.

'No, Harry, integrity is much more than that. Tell me, who is the one person in your organisation you trust blindly?' Jay asked.

I find it difficult to trust people in my organisation, but with some effort, I zeroed in on Ricky. 'I think it is Ricky, the MESA regional CEO of Circo Systems based here in Gurgaon—my boss's boss.'

'Why do you trust him blindly?'

'Because there is something about him… he is very consistent. I have never seen him display his emotions whether things are going bananas or things are going extremely well. He is extremely honest and speaks to everyone with the same candour—be it the senior management or operational staff. He is very honourable and takes care to talk to everyone with respect. I have seen him demolish people's presentations in the boardroom, but he never makes anyone feel inferior,' I said, remembering my various interactions with Ricky.

'That's fantastic, Harry. This guy sounds like a good leader. And what else made you trust him?'

'There was a little incident that remains etched in my memory. Ricky was visiting our office in Mumbai about two years ago and went to fill a glass of water from the cooler on the floor. He came back with the plastic cup of water but before drinking it, asked me where the plastic cups were stored. I was not sure why he wanted to see that, but nevertheless, I took him to the pantry and showed him. He immediately took some and proceeded to the water cooler and placed them in the empty dispenser. I was puzzled and asked him why he did this. His response was surprising. He said he did not feel comfortable taking the last cup and leaving the dispenser empty for the next user. He had spent five minutes of his valuable time to do this, but he did not want to inconvenience his people. Wouldn't you trust such a person?'

Jay was listening with open admiration. 'Absolutely, Harry. This is integrity: *Winners live a consistently principled life, whether someone is watching or not*; whether it is something major or something insignificant. Whether anyone saw Bobby Jones's golf ball move or not, he called a penalty against himself; whether the matter pertained to an insignificant stack of plastic cups in the dispenser or something more important, your regional CEO lives his core values.'

I then remembered another time when I was taken aback by Ricky's honesty. 'About five years back, Ricky, then regional technical director, had accompanied me to meet one of our top prospects in Mumbai, an asset-management firm that had decided to upgrade from a home-grown system to a fully automated system.

'I was then a relationship manager and after months of effort, had finally secured the order. During the signing ceremony for the software solution, the president of the firm asked Ricky whether he was sure our software solution could be implemented in the next three months, in time for the inauguration of their offshore offices. This, in fact, had been a key requirement of the client, but had I explained to them the extensive customisation they wanted would push the implementation to at least five months, they would have cancelled the order. The order was large and I did not want to lose it.

'The value of the order meant that my annual bonus that year would have doubled. And I knew that once the client had signed, he simply would have borne the delay... it happens all the time. I also knew if I did not get the order, a competitor would have bagged it, again by giving a false promise, since no one could have delivered a fully customised solution in three months. Ricky read the technical specifications carefully and, to my shock, explained to the president that our solution was merely a platform that required to be configured based on individual client requirements, and looking at their specifications it would take at least six months to implement the solution. The president was shocked and looked at me disgustedly. He also refused to sign the agreement, and we had to walk out embarrassed. Ricky never said a word to me in front of the client, assuming full personal responsibility for the miscommunication and apologised profusely to the president before leaving.

'On our way back to the office, I was sweating and was sure I would be sacked. But Ricky, as always, did not lose his cool. Probably, he guessed why I had made a false promise to a potential client. He came back to the office, called a meeting of all the staff and explained what had happened. He did not berate me or single me out. He spoke about principles, ethics and core values of the company. He made it clear that Circo Systems would rather lose business than have a single dissatisfied client. He also made it clear that we would pitch our product only on our strengths and never belittle the competition, even if the competitors were lying and giving false promises. That slandering the competition also debases our own position.' I had goose bumps remembering that day.

'But, Jay, short-termism is being forced upon us. If I slip on my quarterly budgets, I would be seriously hauled up by the management!'

'Harry, you have a point. But you always have two choices: to take the easy way out, "be practical" and compromise, or do the right thing and face the consequences. *Living with integrity may lead to short-term pains but leads to long-term gains.* But the good news is that each time you make an uncomfortable but right choice, it makes it easier for the next time,' Jay explained.

'But there will be consequences, Jay,' I debated.

'There will always be consequences of choosing integrity over pragmatism. But it is not difficult for a person like Ricky, who walked away from a very large order rather than compromising his position. The company suffered loss of sales in the short term, but in the long term, he prevented major embarrassment for the company. He stayed true to his core values through the manner in which he conducted himself at the client meeting and later in the office. He ended up having an indelible impact on you. Didn't you say he is the only person in your company you trust blindly?'

I nodded in agreement.

'And isn't that the reason why Ricky was promoted to become the CEO of the region? I am sure Ricky was not the greatest go-getter or the brightest and the most intelligent resource that Circo had at that time, but probably he was the only person who consistently demonstrated integrity, both in his personal and professional life. He was the most trusted to do the right things, to uphold the values of the company and be fair to the employees and all stakeholders. Moreover, your senior management knew Ricky would instantly command the respect of his peers and subordinates,' Jay declared, as though he had worked in Circo Systems and knew exactly how Ricky got promoted!

'You are right, Jay. In those days no one had imagined Ricky would be promoted. He was the most low profile among the potential candidates. He had excellent business acumen, but there were others who were better than him.'

'You know what, all of us have a strong moral compass embedded inside us. If you follow its advice, you have a sure shot at reaching your goal. However, if you ignore it and look for shortcuts, you may lose your goal. Pay attention, *your moral compass always points to the direction of victory*,' Jay asserted.

What Are You Planting?

Jay was moving further on the course as we talked. However, just before the next shot, he stopped and put down his club. 'I will tell you my favourite Zen story on the value of honesty. Being honest is not easy but it builds trust. And trust is always a launchpad for victory.

'There was a wise old king who wanted to appoint a successor. He invited many young boys to his palace for a test. He gave them each a seed and announced that one year later he will select the king based on the plant each one is able to grow from that seed. One of the boys, named Liang, went home excited and planted his seed in a pot filled with fresh soil. He then watered it carefully but even after a few weeks it did not sprout. Some of the other boys started talking about their seeds turning into healthy plants. Liang kept checking his seed, but nothing ever grew. He knew his seed had died.

'A year finally went by and all the boys brought their plants to the king for inspection. Liang took his empty pot and stood at the far end of the hall, scared the king might see and punish him for his failure. The king did spot him with his empty pot and summoned him to the throne. Liang was very nervous. However, to his surprise the king looked very pleased. The king asked him his name and shouted out loud, "Behold everyone, Liang is your new king!"

'The king explained to everyone that one year ago he had given boiled and dead seeds to everyone. He did not want to test their gardening skills. Instead, he wanted to select the most honest and trustworthy candidate. The moral of the story: "If you plant honesty, you will reap trust".'

'Jay, I do understand your point, but we live in a world where the "end justifies the means". I am not going to tell my boss at the end of the year that I lost two sales orders because I was brutally honest with my clients. He only cares about the bottom line,' I said, attempting to justify my work practices.

'Okay, Harry, let us go with your logic and extrapolate it. What would happen if you continue to give false promises?'

'There will be service issues after the sale. But those issues will stay with me. I am managing them and will continue to manage them in the future. No client complaint has ever reached the head office,' I countered.

'What if the discontentment grows? What would happen to

you and your company's reputation? Wouldn't you lose the trust of the market and then slowly lose your leadership position? Think about it… this route is not sustainable. It will give you temporary success, but you will not be able to sustain it for long. Eventually, you will open doors for competition even if they are less competent and more expensive.

'And the growing service issues will drown your organisation and sap you and your people of your energies. Personally, these issues can bog you down, increase stress, and impact your health and family life. I can go on and on about professional and personal consequences of dishonesty.'

Blank Cheques

'In the real world, when people trust you, they will stick with you. When they do not trust you, the relationship is broken. Trust is the foundation of all relationships. And as author Stephen Covey says, trust is a function of competence and character.'

He took the diary again to draw this illustration:

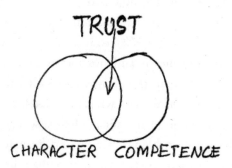

'Competence can be simply defined as your knowledge and skills to deliver results. It is a hard and measurable skillset. Character is defined as integrity—honesty, fairness and good intent. It is a fuzzy concept, not evident on the surface. *Competence plus character equals trust!*

'When I started my career in Delhi, I had an old car that often had problems. In those days I used to always go to the same motor mechanic, Raju Bhai, because I knew he was competent and, more importantly, I knew he would not fool me. One day my car wouldn't start in the morning; it was dead. Trailing it behind my friend's car with a rope, I towed it to Raju Bhai's workshop and was expecting the worst, a huge bill. When he called me later in the day, he said the battery cable was loose and I could come and collect my car—the total bill was zero! Another time when I had problems with the brakes, and was willing to pay for new brake pads, he told me there was no need to change. It just required topping up the brake oil. A year later when I took the car for servicing, he told me that not only the brake pads but even the brake discs needed to be replaced. I paid without any discussion. He now had a blank cheque from me.

'So you see... my motor mechanic was not only making good moral decisions but also sound business decisions. He was focusing on the means and not just the ends. There were many equally competent motor mechanics in the market but Raju Bhai had a character that was unmatched. I was his loyal customer and everyone in my social circle also became his fan. They had all given him blank cheques and he made sure never to lose their trust! Today Raju Bhai owns a chain of auto garages in Delhi and neighbouring cities. Beautiful, isn't it?

'On the golf course every player gives a blank cheque to his opponents—no one goes checking on the other players to see if they played honestly, scored correctly, or marked penalties on themselves. In real life your success will not depend upon your competence alone. Winning in real life will depend upon the number of blank cheques you have received from others—the trust others have placed in you. Think about how many blank cheques you possess, Harry,' Jay said.

I immediately thought about my wife. I didn't think she would give me a blank cheque. She did not even trust me to drop and pick up our kids from a birthday party, let alone trust me with anything more important. I thought about my boss—he for sure was always suspicious about the quality of business coming from my branch. I thought about my customers—very few were coming back for repeat business. I thought about my friends—our pointless and trivial discussions over drinks, complaining about work, gossiping and making fun of others. Were we even friends? After all, we couldn't have a decent conversation till we were two drinks down. I didn't think any one of us could trust the other with a so-called blank cheque.

Did I have a single blank cheque? The thought was troubling. Even though I felt a sudden sense of clarity in my mind, something kept bothering me.

Then I had another flash. The entire foundation of my start-up was built on stealing business that could have been executed by my employer. Since I knew Circo's financial quotation, I could easily undercut and divert that business to my venture. Circo's loss of business would not raise many eyebrows within the company but that business would give a massive kick-start to my company for a few years.

I was convinced about Jay's statement on focusing on 'the means and not just the ends'. Would I ever derive satisfaction and fulfilment from a business that completely disregarded the means and focused on success at any cost?

The answer was an unambiguous no.

Circo had trusted me with a blank cheque, but I was about to misuse it.

And as I was realising this deeply uncomfortable thought, Jay spoke again, '*Competence makes you successful but character keeps you there.*'

It was getting more uncomfortable for me and I had to tell Jay about my own experience with integrity, or the lack of it.

'Jay, I have a confession to make,' I said with a heavy heart.

'Go on,' Jay said.

'Jay, I have lived a life of low integrity. I have done everything that you said respectable people should not do. I have paid bribes to get business so that I can achieve my goals. I have poached customers from my colleagues to surpass them. I have ignored bad behaviour of some of my team members just because they were generating big sales numbers and ignored the damage it did to the overall morale of my office. I have planned to steal business from my own company to start my own venture. I have never respected the efforts of my wife and family and have always ignored them.

'I feel miserable. I am scared I will be caught one day and will be exposed just the way you explained—skeletons tumbling out of my closet. What should I do?' I let everything out, every thought that was making me feel sick of myself.

Jay listened carefully and patiently.

'Harry, your self-awareness itself is half the battle won. Don't worry, what is done is history. You can decide from today to change your ways. You are the master of your destiny.' His words were soothing and reassuring.

I suddenly felt relieved and comforted, as if a huge burden was off my shoulders.

'Come, let us move on. There is another paradox that we must confront!' Jay announced.

Mindset 6: Integrity
Focus on the Means

Winners are confident about their own skills. For them, the means is as important as the end.

Take a shot:
Do you always think about using the right means, rather than just any means, to achieve your goals? Can you think about times when you had to face this dilemma? Think about the times you paid a price in the short term to stick to fair and honest means. Was the end result more fulfilling?

Ace It, but Pace It

Jay saw golf as the perfect metaphor for life, touching every aspect of our living and working spheres. In fact, he believed that 'golf is life and, not only that, it is life condensed.' Over 18 holes on the golf course, a player can experience everything that makes up life. I was enjoying the day, even though I was not really learning to play the game itself. I was mentally making plans to start playing golf as soon as I returned to Mumbai. But most importantly, I was learning so much about the rich lessons golf taught us about living the good life and becoming a winner.

Seeing Jay play with effortless ease was very motivating. I knew very well this level of mastery had been achieved only with years of dedicated practice.

Jay parred the 6th hole. He finished the short 7th hole in 2 shots less than par, which he said was called hitting 'an eagle'. He then completed the dog-legged 8th hole in 1 shot less than par. He explained that the golfer's term for this achievement was 'a birdie'. The 9th hole was again short, a par 3, but was tricky because part of the fairway was taken over by a huge water hazard. Jay played it carefully, saying it was more important to stay in the game rather than becoming a superhero and taking undue risks. On the long 426-yards' 10th hole, with its narrow fairway spattered with hazards all along its length, he had had no choice but to play it safe again.

By the time we completed the 12th hole, it was past 10 a.m.; the mist was gone and the sun was shining brightly above us. Walking for over two hours was already making me a bit weary, and we still had another 6 holes to go. Meanwhile, Jay, who had walked the same distance as me and had hit over 40 strokes during this time, looked as energetic and fresh as he had been at 7 a.m.

I was running out of energy and also sweating. When I asked Jay if we could go back to the clubhouse for a drink, he took out a bottle of orange juice and a pack of biscuits from his golf bag. I slumped on the green of the 12th hole, gobbled some biscuits and gulped down the juice. The dose of glucose gave me an immediate energy boost. Jay looked a little impatient and gave me a helping hand to get back up on my feet. It was very embarrassing to be helped by someone nearly twenty years my senior.

The Paradox of Hard Work

'Jay, golf appears to be physically less challenging than many other sports, but it is quite strenuous,' I confessed.

'You are right, Harry. Do you know a golfer has to walk about eight or nine kilometres while playing 18 holes and it takes about four or five hours to complete the course? During this period they execute between 80 and 100 shots, which not only require physical effort but also a high degree of mental balance and mindfulness. Moreover, golfers are not allowed to take a break while playing—it is against the rules of the game. You have to play continuously and at an even pace. There are a number of teams playing on the course at the same time. If you are playing too slow, the team behind you will catch up and will be held up because of you and if you are too fast, you are likely to bump into the team playing ahead of you on the course.'

'Interesting!'

'Golf is the only field sport where players do not need to run. It is played at an easy but steady pace. Golf does not require brute energy and muscle that many other sports require, but it requires physical and mental stamina and perseverance. People who play with great initial gusto and pomp tire out by the 9th hole and then just drag themselves for the rest of the game without making much impact. Players who lack mental and emotional resilience get bogged down by a few bad shots and then struggle to regain their vigour in the rest of the game.

'You will never see a golfer running. Golfers strike a stationary ball and then walk to the spot where the ball has landed, to play the next shot. It is the number of shots taken to complete the round, not the speed, that decides the winner.'

'And if they increase their speed and start running to complete the hole faster, they will bump into the players who are playing at the track ahead of them,' I said repeating what I had just learnt from Jay.

'Exactly! This is because teams are playing on all the holes simultaneously.

'This set-up of golf makes us walk towards our goals, not rush towards them. Whenever we start rushing in our life, we reduce mindfulness and increase mindlessness. Chances of accidents increase. The slow pace of the game gives clarity of purpose, clarity of plan and clarity of priorities. The easy pace allows space for gaining bigger perspectives, detachment from the outcome and focusing on immediate execution. So here's another message hidden in the format of golf: *Don't chase the future; walk towards it.*'

'Very well said, Jay.'

'Approaching your life with the frenzy of a hundred-metre sprint can drain you of your energy and hence of your creativity and innovativeness, quickly turning your life into a drudgery. Instead, think of golf, and your life, as running a marathon, slow and paced out, conserving energy rather than spending it on trying to achieve a faster speed, not intent on outpacing others, but maintaining a good, even pace, all the while focusing on every step, and planning the next shot, rather than being goal-obsessed.'

'Slow and steady wins the race!' I jumped in.

'I would say smooth and steady wins the marathon, while the fast and furious can at best run a hundred-metre sprint. To win the long race of life, you have to loosen up and take it easy. *A frantic life can take you higher but not very far*—and that sets you up for a fall.

'Let me tell you a little story,' Jay said. 'Once there was a competition between two woodcutters, John and Ben. Both started hacking away on large logs of wood in their own sheds that were within earshot of each other. After an hour, John stopped. Ben was puzzled but carried on chopping.

'Five minutes later, he could again hear the swing of John's axe. Another hour went by, and John again seemed to stop chopping for a few minutes. Ben was thrilled. He became more confident that he would win.

'So he kept chopping away, pausing only to wipe away the perspiration from his forehead. John's "start and stop" continued for the rest of the day, and Ben's delight grew.

'At the end of the day, however, Ben was surprised to discover John had chopped more wood.

'"How can this be? I never stopped chopping once but you kept taking breaks!" cried Ben.

'"Yes, but I stopped to sharpen my axe and rest my muscles," John replied.'

Jay concluded by giving the moral of the tale: 'Hard work without rest and relaxation leads to fall in performance. Time invested in looking after your own self is worth many hours of hard work.'

Balance the Beam

'Yes, I agree with you, Jay. Balancing hard work with rest and relaxation is very important for me. After office, I like to switch off, relax and do nothing, have a few drinks, socialise with friends and forget work. If I get a weekend at home, I try to just laze around or catch up on sleep. That is how I recharge myself for the next day,' I said, sharing my idea of maintaining work-life balance.

'Harry, it is very important to switch off and relax, and it is equally important to socialise with friends. These are absolute essentials for a happy and fulfilled life. I also like the point you mentioned about doing nothing; you should definitely have some time during the day when you do nothing. It is good for the brain. But let me tell you something: what you just described to me cannot be called a balanced life.'

'Why?'

'Because it seems that you live in office, and the rest of the time you are just trying to forget office and escape from it... so, where is the balance?'

'But that is the balance: working hard, partying harder and then resting!' I said laughing, unable to see Jay's point of view.

'You know what, think of a balancing scale. To balance the beam, you have to put equal weights on the two pans. Correct, Harry?'

'Correct,' I echoed.

'If you put all your efforts on the work pan and then put nothing on your personal life pan, the scale will sink towards work and your life will be tossed away—into the sky. So what can you do to add some weight towards the life side of the scale?'

Jay extended his hand for my diary and quickly drew this sketch:

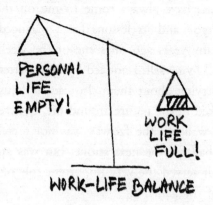

My eyes narrowed as I took in the sketch.

'Jay, you are saying my pursuits are empty and cannot give me any feelings of fulfilment or satisfaction. What do you suggest I do?'

'*An empty personal life cannot balance a full work life.* Fill your life side of the scale with tangible goals and objectives, however simple or small they may be. Put some weight on the personal life side of the balance. Remember, realising small goals leads to fulfilment, satisfaction and a sense of achievement that in turn lead to happiness and wellbeing. So fill your personal life with goals—even if they are small and easy ones.'

'So you're saying I should have specific tasks in my personal life just as I have for my professional life?' I asked.

'Correct. It could be as simple as pursuing a hobby where you can actually set small achievable targets and timelines. Or set an objective of spending quality time with family, but then set clear targets and stick to them.'

'These are good ideas,' I agreed.

'Good ideas have always come to me on the golf course. The game of golf and its lessons for a balanced life came as revelations many years ago on some of the weekends, when I used to play all by myself. I noticed I played better strokes when I stopped worrying about them. Instead, if I just enjoyed the walk and soaked in the nature around me, between the strokes, I realised the walk on the fairway was not merely a means of reaching the ball for the next stroke, but was an integral part of the game. It served the very important role of balancing the two aspects of the game.

'After I realised the importance of balance, one of the first things I did was to enrol for a professional photography course. I had always thought photography was my hobby, but I had never taken it seriously. After attending the course, I really started deriving pleasure from my hobby. It was no longer a casual pursuit. I set a monthly target of at least one photo-walk in the city, clicking and processing a few good pictures, sharing them with photography groups, and then actively seeking critical evaluations from experienced photographers. This upgraded my skills dramatically and many of my pictures have now been published in newspapers and some have even won awards. I still continue my hobby, and I can tell you, it is such a boost to my levels of happiness.'

This man is so talented, I thought. Aloud, I said, 'You sure lead an exciting life, Jay. I can really see how achieving work-life balance can be rewarding.'

'And, Harry, if you want to fill your personal side of the weighing scale with the ultimate level of happiness, you have to think beyond yourself.'

'What is that?'

'You have to start giving—giving back to the society that is providing us with all the luxuries that we and our families are enjoying in our lives.'

'Yes, I do.'

'What can you do to give back to society?' Jay asked.

'Well, on that count, I think I am doing my bit quite well.'

'What is that, Harry?'

'I am regularly donating money to a number of charities that take care of underprivileged children,' I said with pride.

'That is good, but where is your personal involvement in the community other than writing some cheques?'

'What do you mean?' I asked, surprised. I had been expecting a pat on the back from my new mentor.

'Many people in this world find it easy to dole out cash, but only few can donate their time. The community needs both, your money and your time. Let me explain. For the last many years, I have been part of a group of golfers who spend time with poor migrant workers from villages to teach them basic life skills like financial literacy, computer skills, English language, personal health and hygiene. As a result of these efforts, we have seen many workers upgrading from manual labour to much better jobs. Some have now become courier delivery boys, others have become drivers, and yet others have become office assistants and cashiers. Their incomes have gone up manifold. As a result, they can now afford to send their children to good schools. A little intervention can change the destiny of their families and their future generations.'

'Wow, that is such a great achievement,' I said, feeling more admiration for Jay by the minute.

'That is the point. Harry, no amount of money could have made these major differences in the labourers' lives. A little extra money cannot pull them out of the vicious cycle of poverty. The quantum shift that can set them free from this cycle is skill development. That is what our group is trying to achieve.'

'It must be very satisfying to come across these success stories?'

'Absolutely, and that is what I mean by filling up your personal life with solid, result-oriented activities that contribute to your work-life balance. Today, I have many such activities that I pursue in my personal life and I have set a target for each one of them. Over the years, I have seen so many successful people and found one common trait among all of them. Winners really look forward to weekends—not to get away from work, but to get immersed into their rich personal lives. Winners pursue a balanced life—a busy professional life and a rich personal life.'

'That is really nice,' I acknowledged.

'But, Harry, keep in mind that it is all about balancing the scale. It is easy to over-commit to one side of the scale and then to turn around and over-compensate on the other side. For example, you take up a new professional challenge and spend the next one year working day and night in the office, only to realise that you are becoming a stranger to your family. And then you try to make up for it by showering them with expensive gifts or splurging on spectacular vacations, when all they need and want is an engaged spouse and parent. You see the point about balance, Harry? The scale will be balanced only when the weights on the two sides are equal,' Jay added.

'Harry, *sustainable professional success is merely a by-product of a fulfilled personal life.* Additionally, I don't believe professional achievements alone are the true measures of leadership success. An off-balanced success that comes at the expense of your family and personal life, health and happiness is, in fact, a sign of utter failure. Many achieve big results in their professional lives, but the real hallmark of a winner is a fulfilled and flourishing personal life.'

Selfish Is Okay

I was thinking about my own situation. It sounded very similar to what Jay had just stated. My family life had become the sideshow of my overall life. I was living and breathing my work, yet struggling for recognitions and rewards. On the other hand, my health was in shambles.

For the first time in my life, I understood the concept of work-life balance. Even though the term is used so often, most of us don't fully understand it. I now realised having late-night parties or doing nothing and sleeping over the weekend were not balancing my professional life.

And now I appreciated what Jay meant when he said we have to become selfish to become successful. After all, if I could not look after myself, how could I help others, whether at work or at home?

'The weight of your work is not always in your control,' Jay said, 'but what you put into the personal life side of the scale is entirely in your hands. Remember, in the end, it is you who has to balance the scale!

'Personally, to achieve this balance I had to first become selfish.'

'Selfish?' I asked, quite taken aback by the word.

'Yes, I realised if I am not selfish enough to take out some time every day for my physical and mental wellbeing, how can I be a good husband, a good father or a good professional? I would not be able to do justice to my family if I am drained and tired during the time I spend with them. I would not do justice to my work and my colleagues at work if I am not in top physical, mental and emotional shape to handle the responsibilities given to me.'

'They do say you cannot pour from an empty cup,' I interjected.

'So, I say again: I am now very selfish. I think about myself as much as I think about anything else.' He smiled as he said that.

'Harry, have you noticed the safety announcements on an aircraft just before take-off? The stewardess says, "In case of a drop in air pressure in the cabin, oxygen masks will drop down from above your seat. If you are travelling with a child or someone who requires assistance, secure your mask on first, and then assist the other person." Do you know why they say you should help yourself first?'

'Now that I put things in perspective, I get where you're going with this example. A mother is likely to be more worried about her child and will attempt to first place the mask on the child's face. But doing so can endanger the mother herself and if she loses consciousness in the interim, she will not be able to help the child at all. Like you said, if you cannot help yourself, how can you help others?'

'Very good, my boy!'

Jay looked happy. 'Let me ask you another question. You

earn money every month, but do you spend it all?'

That was a weird question, I thought, but answered him nonetheless. 'I spend a lot but I try to invest some for our future—even though most of my investments are not doing well.' I groaned in mock frustration, which got a chuckle out of Jay.

'But you do invest to secure a wealthy future?'

I nodded.

'One more question. How much time do you invest every day on the health of your company, Circo Systems, to make it financially healthy?' Jay asked with a twinkle in his eyes.

'My entire day,' was my prompt answer.

'You are investing money to secure a wealthy future for your family. You are investing time to secure the financial health of your company. What are you investing to secure a healthy future for your own self?' Jay asked with a raised eyebrow.

'Okay, I get it. You have a point there.'

'This is a lesson I learnt from the tragic life of my first boss.'

'What happened?'

'My boss was the head of manufacturing and was completely dedicated to the company. The deadly concoction of work-related stress, late working hours, extensive business travelling, sleep deprivation and alcohol, along with no physical exercise took a toll on his body. He was on a fast track in his career but did not know the track was going to hit a wall. At the age of forty, he had a minor heart attack, but recovered quickly. From then on, he worked hard at improving his lifestyle. From being a social animal that had always lived with the motto of "work hard and party harder", he became disciplined, very conscious of his eating habits, sleep and physical fitness. Some improvements in his health allowed him to work even harder, and with his sharp intellect and acute business acumen, he was soon propelled to the top job of our company, when he was just forty-three. He became the youngest CEO a major industrial group had ever seen.'

'That sounds like a success story,' I commented.

'Unfortunately, it was not. The chief executive's role brought fresh challenges. Now, he was managing a rapidly growing business and a demanding board of directors and shareholders. On the day he was celebrating his forty-fourth birthday, he suffered a stroke that left him paralysed below the hips. Even though his health had improved somewhat with time, the earlier damage to his physical system was permanent. The excesses of his younger years caught up with him just when he was about to take off in his career. Being a CEO at the age of forty-three could have taken him places in his career, but that was not to be.'

I could see the pain on Jay's face as he spoke about his former boss. 'Did he recover from the stroke?'

'He could never recover. Even after months of treatment and physiotherapy, he remained confined to his bed. The company suffered as much as he did. Expecting his recovery, the board of directors kept the CEO's position empty, but with time, that started hampering regular business apart from lowering the morale of the staff and sentiments in the marketplace. Exactly one year after the day of his stroke, on his forty-fifth birthday, the shareholders pulled the plug on him and sent him a relieving letter with a handsome parting bonus. The business he had sacrificed his life for decided not to wait for him anymore.

The fall from being one of the most powerful business figures in business to a physically challenged person was too much for him to handle. He just withered away at home and did not live to see his fiftieth birthday.'

Jay was choking as he spoke. And for the first time, I noticed signs of ageing on his face that was otherwise masked by his trademark serene smile.

'I am very sorry to hear that, Jay. I can imagine the impact that tragedy had on you,' I said, trying to console him.

I could connect to what Jay had said just a few minutes earlier, 'A frantic pace can take you higher but not very far.' My life was as frantic as the life of Jay's boss. I had the same issues—long and stressful working hours, socialising, drinking and little sleep with absolutely no balance in life. Was I heading in the same direction?

The Battle of Brains

Trying to compose himself, Jay took off his glasses, rubbed his face with his hands and changed the topic quickly. 'Have you heard of the fight-or-flight response, Harry?'

Like an eager student, I said, 'Of course. It's how our bodies respond to stressful situations, right?' I was familiar with what Jay was describing.

'Yes, Harry, very often when golf players start having a bad run with their strokes, they get mentally stressed, which further impacts their ability to play good shots. Without the mental strength to deal with the ups and downs of the game, a player will find that a situation can quickly go out of hand and lead to a downward spiral. Isn't this like our life at the workplace?'

'Yes, I agree.'

'Whether it is a bad shot on the golf course that increases the danger of impacting your score, a missed sales order that increases the danger of missing your year-end revenue target, a rash driver in the next lane on the road who is trying to move in front of you, a long queue at the checkout counter in the supermarket or your partner in a foul mood, your brain switches to fight-or-flight mode and puts you into an autopilot, mindless state. So with adrenalin pumping through your blood stream, you are likely to say or do things that you will regret later,' Jay said.

'Very interesting. I can relate to each one of these situations. But is there a way out, Jay?'

'Luckily, a part of the brain is responsible for the reasoning and rationalising abilities in us. This part of the brain is reflective as opposed to the reactive brain. When you are provoked – such as when a colleague says something against you in a meeting or a rash driver crosses you on the road, if you take a deep breath, allowing just enough time for the reasoning part of the brain to overpower the instinctive, reactionary part, you will hold yourself back from lashing out. You will tell yourself that you must first understand why your colleague spoke that way or what you can really do to tackle the menace of rash driving on roads.'

'That explains a lot. I often fail to reason, and simply react without thinking and regret my words and actions later on,' I confessed.

'In the end, *the reflective wins over the reactive.*

'So, the next time an email from a colleague lands in your inbox and you think it requires a befitting harsh response, take a deep breath. The next time someone overtakes your car on the road, almost causing an accident, and you think you should honk, flash lights, chase him and overtake him, take a deep breath and allow the adrenaline rush to pass. Let logic and reason prevail over fight-or-flight emotions. There will be peace,' Jay declared.

The Resilience of the Reeds

'Just like in a game of golf, setbacks and failures are a part and parcel of living and working. In golf, a perfectly executed shot can end up badly and a perfectly bad shot can give you a lucky break. In life, the most planned action can lead to disappointments and the most unplanned action can sometimes open up a world of opportunities. Golf and life are not games of perfection. If we let those bad shots fester and consume us, it will only lead to a bad round.

'Imagine if my golf ball lands up in the sand bunker to the left of the putting green,' Jay said, pointing towards the 15th hole, 'and while chipping the ball out, I hit it harder than required and the ball shoots past the putting hole to the sand bunker on the right of the green, then what can I do?'

'That would be very frustrating,' I remarked.

'Indeed it is and it happens all the time. Either I can start swearing and banging my club on the ground or I remember that golf is a game of life and in life you have to accept many situations as they are. You cannot brood and waste your energy over the past—at times things are beyond your control. Winners learn from every mistake and just move on.

'In fact, there is this famous quote by Ben Hogan, one of the greatest golfers of all times and author of the bestseller *Ben Hogan's Five Lessons*. It sums this attitude of winners: "The most important shot in golf is the next one." Rather than complaining or lamenting, winners accept the present moment. *Fully accepting the present moment without any resistance allows you to focus on progress and growth.*'

'Again, easier said than done,' I protested.

'This brings to mind yet another Aesop's fable,' Jay said, probably to make this concept easier for me.

'I would love to hear it.'

So Jay began. 'A giant oak stood next to a river in which grew some slender and tall, green reeds. When the wind blew, the great oak stood proudly upright with its branches lifted to the sky. But the reeds bowed low in the wind and hustled together.

'The proud oak mocked the reeds. "The slightest breeze on the surface of the water makes you bow your heads, while I, the mighty oak, have always stood upright and faced these winds with my strength."

'"Do not worry about us," replied the reeds. "The winds are strong but do not harm us. The winds are here today, gone tomorrow. However, we have to stay strong and stand tall. Sometimes even the strongest has to take a step back to win."

'As the reeds spoke, a great hurricane rushed towards the river. The oak got furious, its ego was hurt and hence it stood proudly and fought against the storm, while the smart reeds bowed low and got out of the way. The hurricane grew in fury. The oak became more stubborn, and all at once the great tree fell, uprooted from the ground, and lay among the reeds.

'Clearly, the green reeds that kept their ego aside emerged winners.'

Before I could say anything, Jay quickly added, 'I know what you are thinking. Yielding and bowing low may sound subservient and appear as a sign of a loser, correct?'

I was indeed thinking along those lines.

'Look, Harry,' Jay said, 'resilience is the word to describe the reeds. Resilience comes from Latin, which literally means "to spring back". Rather than fighting the reality, living with pride and ego and falling like the oak tree, you can act calmly, take it easy, accept the reality and return to your balance just like the reeds.'

I listened attentively. It was these little asides delivered by Jay that were packed with pearls of wisdom.

'And then there could be significant events that may force us to take a step back. Taking up a lower-paying job after getting laid off from a good one, selling part of your business to stay afloat, ditching a pet project due to budgetary constraints, cutting a large loss-making position in the stock market and other setbacks may all appear to be irreparable and permanent setbacks. But by taking it easy and keeping a cool head, just like the reeds, you could soon bounce back to bigger victories.

'*Winners take it easy,*' Jay declared.

'I also believe *the greatest achievement in life is not winning; it is the ability to recover after a failure.* Many people can win, some by hard work, others by the dint of their intelligence, but when adversity strikes, very few people can actually pull themselves through.

'And we are not talking about big adversities. Everyday occurrences like a professional disagreement with a colleague, an upset customer, spilling coffee on the table, someone breaking the queue ahead of you, getting delayed for an important appointment due to traffic or someone unnecessarily honking at you on the road can sometimes throw us off our emotional balance so much that our entire day can get spoilt. And these are the small things that test your mental strength. If you can overcome these realities and just take it easy, you could be on your way to winning big.'

'Take it easy, got it!' I grinned as I gave him a thumbs-up sign.

'Indeed, it is all in the mind. Success depends upon a number of factors but mental strength trumps them all. Golfing legend Bobby Jones once said, *"Golf is a game played on a five-inch course...the distance between your ears."* It is all in the mind,' Jay repeated, pointing at my head.

We were now walking on the fairway of the next hole. Both of us were quiet for some time. I was digesting all the new insights while my coach Jay looked as pleased as ever—I guess with his strokes and his coaching so far.

After putting the ball, he stopped and asked me for my diary. He then drew this diagram:

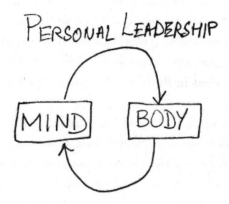

'Harry, both the aspects of personal leadership are interconnected. Mind and body are one continuum—controlling each other.

'This means that our thoughts, feelings and emotions can positively or negatively affect our biological functioning. Negative emotions can make you listless and drag you down physically. Positive feelings can provide energy and vigour to your body. Clearly, our minds can affect how healthy our bodies are! On the other hand, what we do with our physical body—what we eat or drink, how much we sleep and exercise, and even our posture can impact our mental state. A bad state of mind reduces your zest and motivation for life, which can dull our physical habits—this in turn will lead to further deterioration of the mental state, like a vicious spiral.'

Jay made absolute sense. I had a lot to think about. My on-going struggles were clearly because of the lopsided life I lived. I was racing mindlessly. I had to balance my life using so many ideas that Jay had shared. On top of that, my lack of physical fitness and a stressed-out mind, which I now understood are linked to each other, were making it worse for me. I had to work on these aspects using the points explained by Jay. I was fully absorbed in these thoughts and kept following Jay as he played on.

After putting the 15th hole, he stopped. He put his hands on my shoulders and said, 'Harry, look at the beauty of the golf course. You walk on lush green fairways surrounded by high grass on the sides that are swaying with the breeze, leafy trees that dot the landscape and the serene water bodies that are so soothing to the eyes. Isn't it beautiful?'

'Indeed,' I said, enjoying the view.

'But the same course also throws up occasional hazards,' Jay said in a cautionary tone. 'When your shot misfires, the water bodies can gobble up the ball, the high grass can make it difficult to hit a stroke and the sand bunkers can impede your progress.

'Golf teaches us to move forward resolutely towards our objectives but at the same time enjoy the slow and beautiful journey. You will have victories and you will make some mistakes; you will have moments of pleasure and times of grief. All have a purpose and a lesson to teach but you have to continue to move. The beautiful settings have to be fully savoured to make this journey pleasant and meaningful. You do not step on the golf course to simply hit the ball in 18 holes; you play this exceptional game to also enjoy every moment on the course. And life is no different from the golf course.

'Like legendary golfer Ben Hogan said, "*As you walk down*

the fairway of life, you must smell the roses, for you only get to play one round."

As he said these words, a little breeze carried along the whiff of freshly cut grass with it, and I had goose bumps.

Mindset 7: Taking It Easy
Smell the Roses

Winners don't chase the future; they walk towards it.

Take a shot:

Are you living a frantic life? Do you have enough in your personal life to balance your work life?

The next time you are provoked by a situation, a person or your own thoughts, try something new. Try to hold yourself back, take a deep breath, think and reflect patiently before reacting or responding. Can you practise this regularly and observe the magic it brings in your life?

Do you often think about your problems, difficult situations and setbacks? Can you accept them wholeheartedly, forgive yourself and others and just move on? This will unburden you and free yourself to soar higher.

Mindset of a Golfer

Engrossed in all these wonderful and intense discussions, I did not realise when we had reached the 18th hole. On Jay's instructions, I had been noting down the number of shots per hole on the score card. So far, the tally showed he had taken 80 shots to finish 17 holes.

'Harry, the 18th hole on this course is the toughest,' Jay said, as we were standing on the tee area. Beyond the far end of the hole, I could see the magnificent red-brick building of the club house. The plaque next to us read 'Par 4' and '421 yards', the number of shots it should take to putt the ball and the distance between the tee and the hole—which was quite long.

He explained further. 'Even though it looks straight, this is the most difficult to navigate. Not because of the length, but because of the extremely narrow fairway with the lake running parallel on the left side and a large water hazard running almost throughout its length on the right. Even with a little bit of wind, it becomes difficult to land the ball on the fairway. If you are lucky to avoid water and land your ball on the fairway, there are a couple of sand bunkers just before the putting green, another water hazard and then three more sand bunkers on the edges of the green. This final hole is the most exciting one and gives the jitters to even the most seasoned players.'

'I am sure you will ace this one as well,' I said, giving him an encouraging smile.

'I will try my best. All I can do is plan my strategy well and focus on my technique. The rest is not in my hands.'

Picking up some sand from the sides and slowly releasing it in the air, he said, 'There is wind blowing in from the lake, so we have to be careful.' Jay used the 1-wood to tee off, trying to keep the ball as low as possible to avoid the wind. I also noticed from his swing that he was not trying to hit the ball too far, since that would swerve the ball further off-course due to the wind. The ball landed about a hundred yards away, nicely, in the middle of the fairway. In another 3 shots, again short and low, the ball was at the end of the fairway. I could now make out his strategy. He was deliberately hitting low energy shots because he was conscious that longer, lofted shots could sway the ball into the water hazards hugging the two sides of the narrow fairway. He decided to take the extra shots to avoid risks and stay in the game.

On the 5th shot, using an iron to give the ball just enough loft, he crossed the water hazard before landing on the putting green. If Jay had hit a little harder, the ball could have overshot and landed in one of the three sand bunkers. He had calibrated his stroke very well.

Jay was then able to putt the ball in another 2 shots, giving him a score of 7 shots, or 3 over par, on this par-4 hole. His overall score at the end of the 18th hole was 87 shots, or 16 over par, on the par-71 course. He looked very pleased.

It was lunch time when we reached the club house. Jay took me to a restaurant overlooking the golf course. I ordered biryani while Jay asked for pasta. I was famished and quickly gobbled down the delicious rice that had come with yoghurt and pickle.

I felt very thankful to Jay, and for all that had been achieved during the last few hours.

'Jay, I would like to thank you for what you have done for me today. You have introduced me to this magnificent game, but, more importantly, opened my eyes to a whole new universe of managing my life and work. I am not sure if I can thank you enough,' I said.

'Come on, Harry. I enjoyed this time as well. You know what, I love to lecture and today you were at the receiving end,' Jay laughed.

'You're being very modest, Jay. You did not lecture me. You coached me to delve deep into my life and become conscious of what has been going on in my world. You bumped into me—a total stranger, but you have left an indelible mark on my psyche. These few hours on the golf course are going to reset my life. You are a guru.'

'Well, thank you, Harry. I am delighted to know you were able to benefit from the time we spent together.'

'But I have a question, Jay.'

'Go ahead.'

'Why did you do this for me? While on the aircraft, you almost intruded into my life, eavesdropped on my phone calls, you tried to understand my personal and professional situations and then… offered to teach me golf. Why did you do this? You do not know me from Adam!'

'Harry, that is a long story and some other day I will tell you more about myself. But since you have brought it up, let me say, yes, it was not unplanned.'

I scratched my head trying to figure out what he meant but almost immediately, as if trying to change the subject, he said, holding out his palm, 'Show me your diary. You were making a lot of notes.'

'Here you go.' I handed over the diary to him.

He looked through the pages carefully, flipping back and forth, and looked very pleased. He then said, 'Harry, you have made seven pages of notes. Let me explain what these can do for you.'

I knew that the notes carried life-changing ideas for me so I listened carefully.

'Don't you feel you can achieve much more with your life?'

'Don't you feel you can be happier, more content and more productive?'

'Don't you feel you are stuck and not getting the best out of your life?'

I gave Jay an emphatic nod. These were definitely my challenges, and I desperately wanted to overcome them.

'Then from now on you must think like a golfer.'

Taking the pen, he wrote down in the diary:

Seven mindsets for winning like a golfer:

1. Clarity
2. Courage
3. Detachment
4. Excellence
5. Execution
6. Integrity
7. Taking it easy

Handing over the diary back to me, he looked straight into my eyes and stated, 'My boy, you are your best friend and your worst enemy. In life, just like in golf, no one, other than you, can have any impact on your success. Only you can hold yourself back and only you can set yourself free.

'Think like a golfer and realise the personal greatness that lies within you.'

I was a bit overwhelmed and looked through the seven mindsets that he had jotted down in his elegant, long strokes of the pen.

There was silence as he waited for me to absorb his words. At length, he said, 'When you go back to Mumbai, I want you to go through these lessons once again and explore how you can implement them in your life and work.'

'Of course, I will do that, Jay. And I will keep you posted on my progress,' I promised. Indeed, a lot had to be done with my life. I had to completely overhaul it.

We finished lunch and went to the reception area. Jay asked the concierge to order a cab for me.

'Where have you parked your car, Jay?'

'I have come on my Harley.'

'Wow, you ride a Harley Davidson!' I said, very impressed.

'This is a small luxury I indulge in when the weather is good. It is parked there, in the parking lot.' He pointed to the parking area which was one level below the portico.

We shook hands once again before I sat in my cab and waved back at him when the cab started to move. On my way down the road, I saw a massive, red-coloured Harley Davidson gleaming proudly among the cars. Truly, a giant among midgets, just like Jay.

Walk the Course

My head was inundated with Jay's words. Over a few hours that morning, he had downloaded a lifetime of his experience for my benefit. I felt strangely awake. It was as though I had woken up to a whole new world. Having run on autopilot for the last thirty-seven years, for the first time, I felt I could take control of my destiny. The ideas shared by Jay were deep and profound and needed some conscious effort to be implemented. But before working on them, I had to ensure the seven lessons scribbled in the little diary were expanded to a working document. I had to take some time off. I needed time to write everything I had learnt that day and then work on a strategic plan for my life and work. The task ahead of me was very clear.

That evening, during the company dinner, I requested Sid for ten days of leave.

'What? You want to take ten days off?' my boss laughed. 'Are you sure, Harry?' He was pleasantly surprised. It was the first time in many years that I had requested for such a long vacation.

'Yes, Sid. I am sure. Also, during this period, I will not be accessible either on my phone or on email.'

Sid was shocked. This had never happened before.

'Additionally, Sid, during this vacation, I want you to directly supervise my branch.'

Now he looked positively puzzled. He knew that under normal circumstances, I never allowed him to mingle closely with my team, let alone manage them for ten days. But this time was different.

I think he could sense something extraordinary had occurred within me.

'I hope everything is okay? Are you planning to resign, Harry? If that is the case, please give me some advance notice,' Sid said, sounding deeply concerned.

'No, no, not at all, Sid. On the contrary, I am planning something new for our business,' I retorted, immediately on the defensive.

'You and planning...? Since when did you start planning?' Sid said with a chuckle reeking of sarcasm.

Sid was always direct and upfront and never hid his feelings—even more when he was a few drinks down. To a large extent, I guess, his sarcasm was justified. My bias towards action and aversion towards planning was well-known to him. I did not want to push the discussion any further that evening.

'Thank you, Sid. I would like to take your leave now.' We

shook hands and I rushed back to the hotel.

The next morning, as soon as the flight took off from Delhi, I switched on my laptop and started typing in my conversations with Jay. This was the only way to capture the plethora of concepts, ideas and thoughts he had shared with me. I started all the way from our accidental meeting on the flight, the offer to play golf, reaching the golf course on Friday morning and then to the conversations over the 18 holes. I decided to recollect and write down everything while it was still fresh in my mind.

The flight landed on time. On the way home, I continued to type. I reached home to find that Mira and my daughters were at a birthday party and would not be back till late. I kept typing every little detail of our interaction, almost like replaying a movie.

That evening I explained to my wife about my fortuitous meeting with Jay, our discussions over the golf course and what I intended to do about my new-found awareness.

'I am delighted to hear that, Harish. I am happy you have finally woken up. Go for it. No one will disturb you for the next ten days,' she assured me.

To complete writing my notes in ten days, I had to be alert and superefficient. Sleeping at 10 p.m. and waking up at 5 a.m. was one of the first changes in my lifestyle. My cocktail-circle friends were excited about my leave, but I had to politely ignore all their plans for pub-hopping and gambling parties. They formed my comfort zone but robbed me of the time I could spend on personal development and nurturing relations with my family members.

I called up Khosla and told him I was pulling the plug on

our startup. There was no way I wanted to build my venture on dishonesty and deceit. It was a cow I had to let go. Khosla seemed relieved.

It was such a pleasure to having morning tea with Mira, wake up the kids and later drop them to their school bus at 6.30 a.m. Accompanying my wife for a walk and yoga was altogether a new and exhilarating experience. Having dinner together as a family, going for a small stroll in the park and then tucking my daughters into bed were soul-satisfying. I had rarely experienced these aspects of life before. In fact, I had never taken leave and stayed at home like this for many years. Even my daughters were surprised. This had never happened before in their lives. Mira was very pleased but I guess she was watching me carefully, not sure if this was just a passing phase. Seeing her touch wood, probably out of disbelief, many times during the mornings and evenings that we were spending together, I assured her this new lifestyle was here to stay.

Over the next ten days, from eight in the morning till eight in the evening, I completed my notes and jotted down all action points. From my scribblings and Jay's writing and drawings in the little diary, I had put together a massive document—one that laid down the basis of the seven attitudes of greatness, as Jay had called them. Along with them, I wrote down a plan of action for each one of them.

On reaching the office after my long vacation, the team was expecting some frenzied activity, but what they witnessed was a complete antithesis of the Harry they had known. Word had gone around that I had taken a vacation to plan for something really big for our business. Many members of the team came to see me during the day to provide business updates and enquire about my new plans. I assured them they would receive a full briefing from me in the coming week.

Next week, at 9 a.m. on Monday morning, the entire Mumbai branch of Circo Systems checked into the sea-facing conference room on the top floor of The President, close to our office at Nariman Point. The room had been set up specially to accommodate all forty of us around a large conference table. Each person had a file in front of them with a copy of my manuscript.

I started the meeting by announcing, 'Ladies and gentlemen, as you are aware, I took ten days off... to work on a new blueprint for growth and progress. It is called *Think Like a Golfer*. This blueprint contains the seven mindsets for greatness, which have been passed on to me by a corporate guru who made me his student even without me knowing I was under his tutelage.'

I saw people at the conference table look up, a bit amused and a little taken aback by the title of the document. It was quite the opposite of what I had always lectured them about. Normally, they would hear high-pitched war cries like 'Go out and beat the hell out them... crush the competition' or 'Show them who the boss is' and so on. 'Think Like A Golfer' sounded a little odd when my entire management style was built around running or hustling rather than thinking or reflecting! Naturally my team looked a bit confused. I just smiled back.

'Implementation of these mindsets will guarantee that we achieve sustainable, long-term success rather than chasing short-term gains. This will help us to unlock our true personal potential, and together as a team, we will achieve breakthrough success for our company.'

I took a deep breath and continued to speak to the sea of bewildered faces around me. 'These mindsets cover both your personal and work life. You may wonder why I should be talking about your personal life. Isn't that supposed to be your own private affair? The answer is simple: Focusing on one aspect of your life and achieving success in either your personal or professional life is no big deal, but achieving success in both spheres of your life, at the same time, is indeed rocket science. No wonder very few can ever achieve this balance. A lopsided success, by definition, is temporary—a tilted beam is unstable. We are looking at sustainable success and a flourishing life. We want to master this rocket science.'

I waited for this to sink in. 'But luckily, this rocket science has been simplified by my guru—guru of the golf course!'

I saw many people now deep in thought. A few of them were even busy making some notes in their diaries! I felt like a management guru, quite like Jay!

I continued, feeling much more confident now. 'But like everything else worthwhile, this success does not have any shortcuts. It will require dedicated and conscious effort.'

I repeated, 'No shortcuts,' and then, remembering my golf lessons, added, 'only sure shots!'

'The master plan in front of you is straightforward and simple, but not easy. I am fully committed to changing myself and want to support each one of you individually to go through the adjustment phase. There will be short-term consequences, but in the long term, we will all emerge winners.

'We will think like golfers and win like golfers!'

I paused for a while. There was pin-drop silence.

And then I asked them, 'How many of you want to get more from your lives?'

All forty hands went up immediately.

And then sounding like a motivational speaker, I asked again, 'How many of you want to become a better version of yourselves?'

Everyone raised their hands.

'Who wants to experience personal greatness?'

Once again, all forty hands went up in the air. The team was sold on the idea.

'Excellent. In that case, your first task today is to read about these seven mindsets, from the first page till the last. Tomorrow, you will be split into seven teams and each team will work on a detailed execution plan for each of the mindsets. You will come the following day and present your plan to the rest of the teams. We will then discuss, debate and argue the implementation plan for each of the seven aspects of winning, till we reach a conclusion. If we cannot arrive at a consensus on the overall strategy and execution, we will continue the debates for another day. We will not go back to the office till we have all agreed on the way forward. And do not worry about your business. Our sales and service phone lines and email accounts have been forwarded to the Bangalore branch of Circo.'

I saw some heads turning. 'Yes, you heard it right... Bangalore branch, whom we considered our arch rivals, will take care of our business till the time we are here.'

Epilogue

The transformation was magical.

Following well-laid-out strategic goals and plans for our personal lives and work, moving out of our comfort zones, becoming adaptable and flexible, reposing full faith and trust in the process, driven by self-competition, thinking big and acting small, and holding ourselves to the highest degree of honour and integrity while diligently working on our physical and mental well-being dramatically changed the culture of our branch. This new, principled approach of working together ensured that all uncommitted individuals quickly packed their bags and left the organisation. They were replaced by those who were culturally aligned with our new-found values. People started living flourishing lives outside of their work—closely engaged with their families and friends. The culture in the office reflected the positive change at home. As a team, we became amazingly collegial and productive. With time, the results were visible in our day-to-day successes and in the bottom line. As anticipated, there were short-term consequences of the fair way of doing business, but in due course, not only did we catch up on our key objectives, but we went far ahead of our expectations. The new team spirit was palpable and electric!

In a few months, the results of our revolution were visible within Circo and to the wider marketplace, including our clients and competitors. The local and international media quickly picked up the new business model being practised by us. They found our way of working simple and refreshing. Others were more discerning, pointing out that the simplicity and effortlessness of success meant our cultural innovation was very deep and profound. I was invited to television shows, universities and various professional bodies to talk about the new paradigm of fair and balanced success we were practising. I spoke about the profound lessons hidden in the extraordinary game of golf. I was thrilled. Jay's gift was delivering as expected. I sent a couple of emails to Jay, updating him about our success and thanking him for all that he had done for me. But he never responded. Within Circo, perceptions about me and my style of working changed dramatically. My colleagues and seniors from around the world started calling me for my opinions on wider business and organisational-level matters. I became a sort of celebrity. By the end of the year, I was invited to the regional office in Gurgaon to be the chief transformation officer of Circo Systems, a new position that was especially created for me. My mandate was very clear: implement the attitudes of *Think Like a Golfer* all over the region.

We moved to our new home in Gurgaon and I quickly settled down into my new job.

Jay never responded to my emails, so finally, on one Sunday afternoon, after about a month of moving to Gurgaon, I decided to visit Damdama Golf Course, hoping to get some clues about Jay's whereabouts.

I immediately recognised the golf club manager. He was the one who had come and met Jay when we were sitting on the terrace. When I introduced myself and enquired about Jay, he lost his colour.

'Have a seat, sir. What will you have to drink?' he asked, as he averted his eyes.

'No, I am in a hurry. I would like to get his contact details. I have been trying to reach him for a while,' I stated.

'You said your name is Harish Kumar?' he said, while rummaging through a heap of papers in his drawer.

'Yes.'

'You were his guest last January on our golf course?'

'Yes, it was the eighth of January,' I said, not sure what the manager was leading to.

'Oh, I am very sorry!'

My heart sank. I wondered what the matter was.

'What do you mean?'

And then I saw a sigh of relief on the man's face as he found what he was looking for.

'Mr Jagmohan Lal, the president of the Delhi Golf Association, left this envelope for you last month,' and then reading the address he said, 'I was supposed to call Circo Systems and deliver it to you. My sincere apologies, I completely forgot.'

'Is that from Jay?'

'Yes, he is affectionately known as Jay in our golfing community. He is a serial entrepreneur and a leading business consultant.'

I took the envelope from the manager and opened it.

There was a handwritten note that said, 'Congratulations, my boy! You have turned out to be one of my best students and hence I invite you to partner with me in my consulting business. It will be more rewarding than you can imagine. Call me at the earliest.'

And it ended with his phone number.

I rushed to my car and called Jay immediately. He was thrilled to receive my call and we decided to meet soon.

Over the next few meetings, I learnt about the extent of Jay's business and the impact it was having on individuals and companies.

I shared my excitement with my wife, who immediately understood the direction I was about to take. She was fully supportive.

A week later, I explained my situation to my seniors at Circo Systems and submitted my resignation. They understood where I was coming from, and before I completed my notice period, they offered Jay and me a consulting contract to transform the culture of the company, worldwide. That worked out very well for us and for the firm. In due course, other large companies started approaching us to work with their people and revolutionise their workplaces.

Today, I work hard, spend a lot of time with my family, and travel the world consulting for large corporates. *Think Like a Golfer* has created a buzz in the professional world and a competitive advantage for enlightened organisations. Professionals have realised that success earned with the strength of character and power of moral stature is the real victory that leads to fulfilment and happiness in the long run. The shareholders and management of large corporates have realised that their aggressive, success-at-any-cost, vulture-like approach to business can only lead to small, myopic and short-lived victories that come at a heavy cost to long-term reputation and sustenance. A holistic, balanced and integrated approach to living and working is the only path to sustainable success for people, organisations and the society at large.

But as I go about my busy schedule, I always stay on the lookout for young professionals who are struggling—as I was a while back—and make sure I take them for a round of golf.

About the Author

Deepak Mehra is the author of *Ready, Steady, Go!* published in 2015, which has helped thousands of professionals to jumpstart and fast track their careers. The book proposed a number of rules for extraordinary success and one of those was 'Think Like a Golfer'. In his new book, Deepak has extended this concept further to address more profound matters concerning self-mastery and personal greatness.

Deepak's inspiration to write comes from his parents, both published authors in their own fields. However, the inspiration to write *Think Like a Golfer* came from his late father-in-law, an exceptional corporate leader who had introduced him to the unique game of golf. That inspiration translated into the concept for this book when, in the summer of 2016, Deepak crossed the seven-hundred-year-old Swilcan Bridge, between the first and the eighteenth fairway of the Old Course at St Andrews, the birthplace of golf.

Deepak has over thirty years of banking experience in various leadership positions in India and overseas, with leading international and local banks. Throughout his career, Deepak has been involved in coaching and mentoring high-calibre professionals and helping them unlock their true potential. This extensive experience of working with and observing people has given him a deep insight into skills and attitudes that lead to sustainable success in life and work.

Born in Lucknow in 1967 and educated at six different schools in various cities, Deepak graduated from IIT Varanasi in 1989 and secured a management degree from IMT Ghaziabad in 1991. He is a regular speaker at international seminars, conferences, and radio and television on diverse subjects ranging from global capital markets, investments, business management and leadership to happiness and spirituality. He lives in Dubai with his wife and two daughters.

He can be reached on deepakmehra1967@gmail.com.

Acknowledgements

First and foremost, I would like to thank you, the reader, for picking up this book. *Think Like a Golfer, Win Like a Golfer* is full of life-changing ideas and practical wisdom that will help you go from where you are to where you want to be—be it in your relationships, your life, or your career.

This book has taken over five years to write, and even after that it would have probably stayed on my laptop had it not been for my literary agent Suhail Mathur, who helped me to find a top-notch publisher. Thank you, Suhail and The Book Bakers, for your valuable inputs and efforts.

I would like to thank my publisher, Amaryllis, for believing in the concept and bringing it to the readers. Thank you, Rashmi Menon, Bidisha Srivastava and Archana Ramachandran, for your valuable contributions to the book.

I would like to thank my father, Kulyash Rai Mehra, my daughter, Shreea, and my colleague Rohit Singh, who took the pains of reading various drafts of the manuscript and giving critical inputs that were immensely helpful in improving the content.